SALVATION

SALVATION

Antony Hornyold

For Denise,
with love from,
Antony.

April 2022

Anthony Eyre
MOUNT ORLEANS PRESS

Published in Great Britain in 2022
by Anthony Eyre, Mount Orleans Press
23 High Street, Cricklade SN6 6AP
www.anthonyeyre.com

© Antony Hornyold 2022

ISBN 978-1-912945-36-8

A CIP record for this book is available
from the British Library

Printed in Poland

To Caroline

'A great windstorm arose, and the waves beat into the boat, so that the boat was already being swamped. But he was in the stern, asleep on the cushion; and they woke him up and said to him, "Teacher, do you not care that we are perishing?" He woke up and rebuked the wind, and said to the sea, "Peace! Be still!" Then the wind ceased, and there was dead calm,'

(Mark, Ch 4: 37-39)

I

SCAREDY-CAT

Eternal Father, strong to save,
Whose arm doth bond the restless wave,
Who bidd'st the mighty ocean deep,
Its own appointed limits keep:
Oh hear us when we cry to thee
For those in peril on the sea.

William Whiting, 1860

This was Ralph Sebright's third visit to the Holy City. He was a twenty-first-century pilgrim—an elderly pilgrim at that; his short-term memory was failing, though his memory of the distant past remained clear. On his first visit in 1947 he had been a young officer in the British Army, and Jerusalem was in British hands. On his second visit in 1958 he was a British aid official, and the city was divided between Jordanians and Israelis. Now the whole city was in Israeli hands, but he was pleased to be back. However, the downside was that in 2017 the violent dispute between Arabs and Jews, in which he had been caught up on his first visit, continued as bitter and intermittently bloody as ever.

The day after his arrival he woke early. The air was fresh; this was unsurprising given Jerusalem's altitude and it being mid-October. During the morning his group of pilgrims visited the Holocaust Museum at Yad Vashem. The museum was in the form of a long corridor made up of exhibition halls containing various haunting images of the Holocaust. There were old films, one of Hitler making an anti-Semitic speech, underlining the power of the word to arouse hatred. Another, which Ralph found evocative, was a film of children saying goodbye to their parents, mostly forever, at the railway station in Vienna in 1938. It was a different world then, he thought, and the children surely belonged to a bygone age and yet, he realized with a shock, they were mostly born about the same time as himself. He seemed to have been standing for a long time and, feeling a bit tired, found a bench outside the museum where he could wait for the rest of his group to emerge. Sitting in the sunshine he dozed off.

★★★

Ralph woke up to a damp, grey September morning in London. He knew there was something bad about it. Then he remembered that he was to be parted from his mother. He dressed and had a quick breakfast before returning to his bedroom to finish packing. He had barely done this before a taxi drew up outside their house in Kensington. It contained two girls and a middle-aged lady. The girls, Veronica and Juliet, were daughters of a friend of his mother's and the lady, Miss Wood, was their governess. The girls were nice enough, but he did not wish to accompany them to Canada. As an only child, his contemporaries were important to him and his best friends attended the same prep school near Oxford as he did. He neither wished to lose them nor be branded a 'scaredy-cat', a name which had been applied to other boys at his school who had announced that they were being sent abroad to escape the war. Moreover, having not yet fully recovered from the shock of his father's death three years before, he did not now wish to be parted from his mother.

Ralph had listened to Chamberlain's words over the wireless on Sunday 3rd September 1939: 'so now we are at war with Germany'. He was on holiday from school, staying with his grandmother in the Lake District at the time. War sounded exciting to him, but he quickly noticed that the grown-ups in the room had all looked depressed by the news.

Over the next few days nothing much happened except that everyone in the house had to go into town to be issued with a gas mask. Households were told that to guard against the possibility of air raids they must make sure that no light was showing from their home after dark. Blackout material was sewn on to curtains and Ralph was given the job of going outside and checking that no chinks of light could be seen. Air-raid wardens, in the case of their family the local gamekeeper whom Ralph knew well, were appointed to carry out checks at night and reprimand any householder whose lights were showing.

Back at school there were occasional air-raid warnings since Oxford, close by, was a target. On the alarm sounding at night, the boys were woken up and assembled in their dressing gowns in a large basement room. Cocoa and biscuits were provided and the headmaster or another master led them in singing songs. They were never there for more than an hour. No bombs fell near them and they were given a lie-in the next morning. Ralph and his friends looked forward to air raids.

Ralph was conscious in the spring and early summer of 1940 that things were going badly for Britain and her allies. First Denmark, then Belgium and Holland, followed by France in June, had fallen while British troops had been evacuated from Dunkirk. Nevertheless, he was shocked when, during the holidays in early August 1940, his mother told him that he was to be sent to Canada in a week or two's time. Up to then it had not occurred to him that the war could affect his own life. His mother said that his cousins in Vancouver had invited him to stay with them. She had been invited too, but she thought that her duty was to remain in England and support her new husband, Ralph's stepfather, who was engaged in important work for the Foreign Office.

Ralph was deeply disturbed by his mother's decision but, aged twelve, it did not occur to him to challenge it. Nor was he concerned, at least consciously, that his mother's support for his stepfather took precedence over her support for himself. While he did not want to leave her or his school, he could not help being excited at the prospect of seeing a new continent. He knew Canada contained vast forests and fast-flowing rivers, along with moose and bears. His father, Charles Sebright, had travelled much and had whetted Ralph's appetite for adventure with tales of Africa and the Middle East.

During August arrangements were being made for Ralph's departure, the date of which would not be known until a few days beforehand for security reasons. When his uncle came to a goodbye lunch and raised the subject of attacks on British shipping, Ralph's mother got cross. However, Ralph had given no thought to the risk of travelling by sea in time of war.

It was not until the second week in September that his mother was informed of the date that Ralph's ship would be sailing. He had only travelled abroad once before, to the South of France, in the winter of 1937 after his father's death. That time he and his mother had crossed from Dover to Calais. However, by now the Channel ports were being heavily bombed and were considered too dangerous so the Ellerman Line ship, on which Ralph was booked, was departing from Liverpool.

Ralph and his mother had agreed to part in London rather than undergo a long goodbye over the train journey to

Liverpool. Despite being in her mid-forties his mother was slim and youthful looking with no strands of grey in her dark brown hair. Invariably elegant, that day she was wearing a tweed coat and skirt. She enjoyed life and her lips seemed to be always on the point of smiling. However, while Ralph loved her, he found it difficult to talk to her intimately.

This could partly be explained by their having lived, albeit in the same house, largely separate lives. Although his parents had not been rich, they were comfortably off and, as was then the custom for such families, they had employed first a nanny and then a French governess to look after him. He had seen far more of each of these than he had of his parents, who were often away racing at Newmarket or staying with friends. His nanny had been kind and always smiling but she was replaced, when he was six, by a French governess who only smiled when his parents were present. As soon as they were out of the room a hard look returned to her face and he learnt not to meet her eye, for to do so always drew some negative comment. Over three years he had responded by suppressing his emotions and putting up a bland front. When the time came for her to depart, it having been decided to send him to boarding school, he had felt great relief. And when he and his mother had said goodbye to her, without any warmth on his side, he had vowed to avoid getting into the power of such a woman again.

Now it was time for him to part with his mother—his stepfather, whom as yet he hardly knew, was abroad on Foreign Office business. They stood together in the hall, neither knowing quite what to say. She kissed him and said, 'Goodbye, darling, it won't be for long.' Then opening the front door she went out onto the steps to greet Miss Wood and the girls. Ralph gave his suitcase to the taxi driver and, keeping his knapsack with him, got into the taxi. As the taxi drove away, he and his mother exchanged waves.

Having put a brave face on their goodbyes, Ralph experienced the downside as the finality of parting for an indefinite period sank in. He felt sad and alone despite his travelling companions. The girls were also subdued. At one point he smiled for reassurance at Miss Wood but got nothing back. Perhaps she had not noticed or maybe she was too immersed in her own worries. They reached Liverpool in the evening and took a taxi to the Adelphi Hotel, where they were to spend the night, since they were not due to board until the next day. Liverpool had already been bombed, and that night there was an air raid and they had to shelter in the hotel's underground Turkish baths.

In the morning a bus took them from the hotel to the docks. When they got there a siren sounded and they were delayed in a shelter for an hour until receiving the all-clear. Then, after completing formalities, they filed up the gangplank with a lot of other children. Ralph discovered that most of these were being evacuated under CORB, a state scheme which, in response to invitations from the Dominions, was sending overseas children between the ages of five and sixteen. Parents were not allowed to accompany them, so they were in the same position as himself.

On board, Ralph was given a lifebelt in exchange for his gas mask and told to keep it with him at all times. He became aware of the smell, peculiar to ships, of tar, scrubbed decks, and saltwater. He was separated from Miss Wood and the girls, who had their own cabin; he was directed to a larger cabin some distance away for boys. It contained six bunks, and the five other occupants who were already there were children travelling under the CORB scheme.

Ralph said hello to them and they smiled at each other. They were all excited at the prospect of Canada. It seemed a great adventure. None of them knew who they would be staying with on arrival. Ralph at least knew he would be staying with cousins although he had never met them. The oldest of the five, called

Ronnie, was thirteen and from the East End of London. Small and dark, he struck Ralph as being terrier-like, friendly, busy and curious. 'Look at this,' he said, passing Ralph a copy of the ship's menu. It was mouth-watering to those used to wartime rationing. Ronnie had discovered that the ship would be sailing the next day in a convoy which included two destroyers. With other boys of his age Ralph, for the first time since leaving London, began to feel cheerful.

Their ship was nearly new and seemed luxurious to Ralph. It had been built for the India run so while the officers and petty officers were British, the remainder of the crew were Indians, known as lascars.

While Ralph and Ronnie were talking a young man looked in on them. He turned out to be the boys' escort, a young Catholic priest known as Father John. The children being evacuated under CORB were allocated an adult to look after them for the duration of the voyage, generally one escort to about ten children. Father John smiled at them and said, 'We are having a boat drill at 5 p.m. We must all assemble on deck next to our lifeboat which I will show you now.' They followed him up on deck. Father John also told them to have shoes and warm clothes ready by their bunks in case of an emergency at night. Ralph felt slightly uneasy as he remembered, for the first time since coming on board, his uncle's remark at their goodbye lunch about the German threat to British shipping.

They sailed the next day and once at sea Ralph noted two vessels on either side of them. He assumed they were there to pick people up in the unlikely event of the ship being sunk. Their presence was reassuring.

According to Ronnie, who was well-informed about everything, the main threat came from U-boats, but they were also at risk from mines and Focke-Wulf fighters. Ralph was not too concerned, although, from conversations he overheard, some of the adults were. Meanwhile, the meals were excellent and included unlimited ice cream. He ate with Miss Wood and the girls. Veronica was a year older than him and Juliet a year younger. Like him they were going to stay with cousins in Canada; in their case, these lived near Toronto. He found the girls kind and friendly. Perhaps they were sorry for him being on his own.

The crew had fixed up a cricket net on deck for the boys to practise their bowling and batting. An officer, realizing that Ralph was keen, took the trouble to give him encouragement and advice. Ralph appreciated his kindness. There was also a heated swimming pool though, as the ship rolled, he had to take care not to be dashed against the side. He and his cabin-mates were enjoying the voyage.

After the first three days had passed without incident the adults on the boat seemed to become more relaxed. Ralph heard one of the escorts say that, while they would not be completely safe until they reached the St Lawrence River, they were out of the area of greatest risk. Montreal was only five days' cruising away, and the boys in Ralph's cabin talked a lot about what their lives would be like in Canada.

Ralph went to bed about nine but could not get to sleep. Frustrated, he looked at his watch which said a quarter to ten. A few minutes later he heard a heavy thud and found himself on the floor. There followed the noise of breaking glass and wood. The ship shuddered, the lights in the alleyway outside the cabin went out, alarm bells started ringing and Ralph could smell fumes. There was no time to think. The others were by now wide awake and trying to find their warm clothes. However, the initial shock had thrown everything around and it was difficult to find anything in the darkness. Moments later Father John arrived, breathless. 'Follow me at once,' he said. There was an urgency in his voice which brooked no delay.

As they reached the deck, after clambering through a partially blocked alleyway to get to the stairs, Ralph heard an adult say, 'It's alright, it's only a torpedo.' Such inanity at any other time would have amused him, but that night he felt too frightened to appreciate it. Once on deck, and before they had even reached their boat station, an officer ordered them to get into a lifeboat. Ralph thought of Miss Wood and the girls but, as their cabin was forward and the torpedo must have struck the ship aft, he assumed that they would have got to their boat station and been put in a different lifeboat.

He, his cabin-mates and Father John crouched in the boat along with some British and Indian sailors. One of the last to join them, and the only woman among them, was Kathy, another escort. She had gone back below to check that none of her charges had been left behind and had got separated from her group whom, she was assured, were already on another lifeboat.

Ralph's past experience had led him to trust adults in authority. However, as their lifeboat hung for what seemed an age, swinging from the davits, he began to have doubts. He could hear creaking and shouts as other boats were being lowered into the rough sea. The first indication that everything was not under control came when one of the boats capsized as it entered the water, tipping its occupants, including some screaming children, into the sea. When their own boat was eventually lowered the bow dropped with an alarming lurch, leaving Ralph looking down into the heaving black water. It seemed they were about to meet the same fate as the children in the other boat and for a few terrifying moments, during which Ralph had to cling on, the boat remained at an angle. Then, to his huge relief, it righted itself and settled into the water.

Soon they cast off from the liner. It was rough and a full moon appeared briefly from behind clouds. As they pulled away, they picked up an exhausted young naval cadet from the sea who had been trying to rescue people. There were pathetic cries for help which they could not respond to, being already overloaded. After what, to them, cold and uncomfortable, seemed an age, they heard a harsh rending noise and the liner went down stern first with lights ablaze. Although Ralph was expecting this, it was still a shock to see their last link with comfort and safety disappear beneath the waves. Soon after he became aware of a foul stench of oil coming off the water and he could see no sign of the two escorting vessels. One of these, they shortly discovered when they were hailed by a lifeboat containing members of its crew, had also been sunk. They were on their own.

The night seemed endless and it was bitterly cold. In the rush to leave the cabin, Ralph had been unable to find his warm clothes and was dressed only in his pyjamas and the kapok life jacket he had been issued with. By the light of an intermittent moon the black waves looked immense and threatening. Sleep was impossible. He imagined that ships must be on their way to rescue them. But why on earth, he asked himself, had he abandoned his comfortable bedroom in Kensington for this?

This line of thought was interrupted by a British sailor, the steward as it turned out, saying, 'Drink this. It will warm you up.' Ralph gratefully accepted the tiny dipper and took a sip of brandy. He recognized the flavour from Christmas puddings. It was indeed warming.

Dawn came eventually with a rising wind and high seas. As the boat rose to the crest of a wave Ralph could see that there was no vessel in sight, no other lifeboats, not even a raft. Only the occasional piece of wreckage went bobbing by as if to taunt them. He was now able to look round the boat. It was open with a mast, about the length of a London bus, and very crowded. They were so crammed together that it was impossible for anyone feeling seasick to get to the side of the boat. Ralph and his five cabin-mates were the only children. He discovered later that the balance of the forty-six people on board was made up of thirty-seven sailors—five British and thirty-two Indians, a company director and the two escorts. Father John, who had been sick for two days before the sinking, was now incapacitated and could only lie in the bottom of the boat. None of them were dressed to meet an Atlantic storm in an open boat.

Ralph had noticed that during the night the sailors had been pulling handles backwards and forwards and assumed that these were propelling the boat. On enquiring, he was told that this was so and that the handles revolved a screw under the rudder and had to be pulled to keep the boat heading into the waves to prevent it from being swamped. The one British naval officer on board asked for volunteers to work the handles and both Ralph and Ronnie offered to do so—it helped them keep warm. The other boys, whose ages ranged from eight to ten, were not strong enough.

With daylight Ralph's spirits rose, as did everyone else's. It seemed certain that a destroyer would pick them up that day. Meanwhile, according to a remark he had overheard, their boat was setting an eastward course for the nearest land, Ireland, estimated to be some six hundred miles away. At midday the steward served a dipper-full of water (not quite a quarter of a pint) and a single sardine on a ship's biscuit. Ralph was already getting thirsty, but the steward told them he needed to conserve supplies.

The steward was friendly and did his best to cheer them up. He put a canvas awning over the bows under which Ralph, the other boys and Kathy could shelter. However, they remained packed tightly together. Apart from the extreme discomfort this caused, Ralph found that time dragged, as it did for all of the boys, especially the younger ones. There were no books on board but, to make the time pass, Kathy offered to recount what she could remember of the adventures of Bulldog Drummond.

It was kind of her, Ralph thought, and they all enjoyed hearing of the Bulldog's exploits.

Ralph looked at Kathy while she was speaking. Although she seemed no longer young to him, her face, with its pale complexion framed by dark hair, was striking. But it was her calm brown eyes that particularly attracted him. When she smiled at him he could feel some of the fear and tension leave him. She also had a lovely voice and led them in singing songs. 'Roll Out the Barrel', 'There'll Always be an England' and 'Run Rabbit Run' were their favourites.

During the first day a constant watch was kept for smoke from a funnel or the speck of a seaplane. The boys were asked to help with this. Ralph took his turn to stand beside the mast and scan the horizon. Throughout the day there was no sight of a vessel or any living thing except for seagulls, which followed the boat soaring and crying.

That evening, Ralph heard Father John say to Kathy in French—of which his governess had at least left him a good knowledge—that he believed any destroyer that had come back to the scene of the sinking must somehow have missed them. Perhaps, through their exertions with the handles, they had moved too far away. Ralph realized he was not meant to have understood what they were saying, which only added to his disquiet. They were alone in the vastness of the Atlantic under continual attack from the waves, facing the cold and stinging spray, with the wind howling and the mast creaking, and always an exhausting shaking motion.

Once again, the night seemed endless. Ralph, sharing a blanket with Ronnie and another boy, managed to sleep a bit but most of the adults did not. At one point Ronnie woke up with a start, waking Ralph who asked him if he was alright. 'Sorry to disturb you,' Ronnie said. 'Our street got bombed a few days ago and one of my friends was killed. I can't get it out of my mind.'

'I can understand,' Ralph said. 'I have had to go to shelters a few times, but no bombs ever fell near us.' Ralph realized that behind Ronnie's cheerful front lay tension and sadness.

By the next morning the wind had dropped sufficiently for them to hoist a sail and the boat achieved a good speed, which cheered everyone. However, it did not make up for the lack of breakfast, the steward having decided that, given their limited supplies, their first meal should be at noon. It comprised a dipper of water and bully beef on a ship's biscuit. Ralph found that without more fluid the biscuit was too dry to eat, though he enjoyed the beef.

The boys talked about their favourite food and what they would like on landing. Roast beef and Yorkshire pudding came top, with Ralph's selection of fried eggs, bacon and sausages for breakfast a close second. They also talked about their families. One worry was that the pocket money they had been given by their parents as parting presents had all gone down with the liner. They were much cheered when the company director on board, having listened to their concerns, promised on their return to land to make up all the pocket money they had lost.

The boys discussed their predicament and whether it was better to be bombed at home or torpedoed at sea. Ralph and most of the others thought it was better to be bombed since it was over quicker. Ronnie did not comment. Kathy took the initiative to introduce some games: 'Animal, vegetable and mineral' and 'I spy with my little eye'—despite the dearth of objects. She was also asked for more of Bulldog Drummond's exploits. Ralph realized that she had run out of memories and was having to invent new adventures for him. He could see that she was finding this difficult. With little food or sleep, she must have been becoming increasingly tired, as he was himself.

Keeping clean was hard and the boys made do with handkerchiefs dipped in seawater to wipe their faces. Ralph had a comb which he lent out. For calls of nature a bucket was passed round. No one could move from the spot where they were situated so neighbours just looked away. However, with little intake of food or water, this became progressively less of an embarrassment.

That evening before dark a tin of condensed milk was passed round for each person to have a suck. Father John, who was still ill, led them in reciting the Lord's Prayer. Afterwards he asked the boys to say their own prayers. Ralph had been brought up to say prayers before going to bed each night and while at school his headmaster, a strong Anglican, had held morning prayers, including the singing of a hymn—there was one about the sea Ralph particularly liked. Ralph remembered how the wind and the waves had been calmed by Jesus in the Sea of Galilee when the Apostles appealed to him for help, and that evening he prayed that Jesus would come to their aid.

Ralph found the night very cold and uncomfortable, and two of the smaller boys struggled to hold back their tears. Kathy told them to imagine how Bulldog Drummond would have reacted in their situation and that they were lucky to be involved in such an adventure.

By the fourth day Ralph's feet and legs were hurting. They had been wet and cold ever since the sinking and, without exercise, had become numb. He told Kathy, who offered to massage them as she had done, she said, the hands of some of her piano pupils in the past. Her touch eased the pain and was comforting. Notwithstanding, he felt too weak to continue taking his turn at operating the handles.

Ralph's morale was not helped by having overheard the night before two adults expressing their worries over the dwindling supplies of food and water, their ignorance of the boat's position and their doubts about reaching Ireland alive. He felt his strength ebbing away and there was nothing he could do to stop it. He did not want his life to end when it had only just begun.

However, he had to accept that it might end and his thoughts turned to his father. He wished he had been old enough to get to know him better and learn from him. His father had been through the First World War in France and, as a second lieutenant, had been Mentioned in Despatches, but Ralph knew nothing of his experiences there. He thought too of his mother. If he died, it was good that she had remarried. Of the other influences in his life, his nanny and governess, he now wished he had been more forgiving in parting from the latter. He remembered that she had once brought him back some sugared almonds after her holidays in France. Perhaps she had not wanted to be a governess.

By the fifth day no one could eat their biscuits, their throats being too parched. Thirst was the enemy. Ralph's throat was painfully swollen and his tongue felt dry and rough. At times it rained and hailed, and on these occasions they tried to catch the drops in empty tins. The Indians were beginning to grow surly—sick and depressed rather than mutinous.

That night they experienced a violent storm. They took down the sail and put out the sea anchor, but water came in and the Indians had to bail out. Ralph had become used to living with fear, but this was more immediate and terrifying with seawater sloshing around the bottom of the boat. The boys were frightened and seasick. At times it seemed they would be swamped but unaccountably they were still afloat the next morning.

It was Sunday and the steward said he was going to give them a treat. It comprised a small portion of juicy tinned fruit. Despite their cracked lips it tasted wonderful. That afternoon Ralph, whose turn it was to act as a lookout, sighted a steamer. At first a speck on the horizon, it gradually grew and, as if to prove it was no hallucination, a tiny plume of smoke appeared above it. Kathy sacrificed her white petticoat, the brightest object available, to tie to the masthead. There was wild excitement on the boat. Father

John asked the boys to pray that their boat would be sighted. The steamer, a cargo vessel as it turned out, continued to come towards them. Eventually it stopped and turned broadside on. One of the sailors removed the awning over the bows and the stanchions that supported it to facilitate the expected transfer of the boys to the steamer. Their ordeal was over, just in time, as dark clouds ahead heralded the approach of another storm.

Then it happened. As if in some ghastly nightmare the steamer swung round, her propellers churning, and slowly and deliberately departed. They watched in horror and dismay until she had disappeared over the horizon. What reason was there for such an inhuman act? Someone said that U-boats had been known to disguise themselves as lifeboats to attract ships into their orbit before sinking them. But this seemed an unlikely explanation in their case given that the steamer had come so close as to be within sight of the bedraggled occupants of the lifeboat before turning away.

This was their worst moment. The wind and the waves seemed to assume a malign presence and, as if rejoicing at their failed escape, attacked them with renewed fury. Ralph remembered the references to the sea as the enemy in his readings of the Bible at school. He had been puzzled by them then but now he understood. The steward, trying to cheer them, had said that the presence of the steamer indicated that they were in the sea lanes and that it was only a matter of time before they would be picked up by another ship, but Ralph doubted this.

He felt like a prisoner under sentence of death, led to believe he had been reprieved, only to discover suddenly that his execution was about to go ahead. Why had God allowed this to happen? Then he remembered that it was the Germans who had sunk them and other people who had just abandoned them to the storm, whereas God and the sailors had so far kept them afloat. He prayed that they would continue to do so.

24

Throughout the night a ding-dong battle raged between the malevolent sea and their little boat and its occupants. Time and again disaster threatened in the form of a huge roller, only for the boat somehow to ride it. Ralph, who could not sleep, saw it as a struggle between good and evil.

They survived the night with the aid of the sea anchor again, but the boat took a terrible buffeting and by morning those in it were suffering from exhaustion. Some of the Indians, who felt the cold more than the Europeans, lay at the bottom of the boat too weak to move or to operate the handles. Late in the afternoon they thought they saw land ahead. A dark ridge appeared on the horizon and Ralph imagined he could see distant flashes and hear explosions. However, in the morning, their expectations were disappointed for in every direction there was nothing but pale grey sea. A cloud must have deluded them.

During the night one of the smaller boys had become delirious with sharp pains in his feet. Kathy rubbed them to restore circulation. Ralph felt himself weakening. He had eaten little for five days and his thirst was acute. He had noticed with alarm the semi-conscious state of some of the Indians. They had been in the lifeboat for a week.

The day passed and concluded for the boys with a further story from Kathy. Ralph could see that her lips were cracked and that she was finding speech difficult. During the night another of the small boys became delirious. Screaming and shouting, he seemed to imagine himself in prison. Perhaps in the moonlight he had mistaken the shadow cast by the rigging for bars. The officer on the tiller, alarmed that the boy's cries might send the Indians over the edge, told the escorts to keep him quiet. Ralph heard Father John say to Kathy, '*Cet garçon meurt de soif.*' Father John took the boy in his arms and said the prayers for the sick. His low voice and the Latin words seemed to have a soothing effect.

When Ralph woke the sea was calm and the sky clear for the first time since their sinking. The boat was under sail again but there was only a light breeze. Even for the exhausted and thirsty this change in the weather was exhilarating. Kathy took down the awning so the boys could sit in the sun. After the steward had distributed a portion of tinned salmon at noon, Ronnie suddenly cried out, 'Sunderland.' It was true. A tiny speck in the distance grew larger and the white petticoat was again quickly put at the masthead. The flying boat was coming straight for them. Circling, it swooped low and the helmeted pilot leaned out and waved. They waved back enthusiastically. Then the Sunderland headed off eastwards. Ralph's reason told him they were saved but he still could not entirely remove the fear of further disappointment. His confidence had been so shaken by the cargo vessel that had left them at the mercy of the oncoming storm.

However, before long another Sunderland appeared and this time dropped them a parcel wrapped up in a life jacket. The parcel contained a note saying that a destroyer was coming to pick them up, and even better enclosed some baked beans, tinned salmon and peaches. They feasted although the steward, perhaps like Ralph, fearing some further hitch, refused to issue the last of the water on the grounds that they were not rescued yet.

But their luck had changed with the chance sighting of the lifeboat by the Sunderland on a patrol over the Atlantic. A few hours later they saw the destroyer approaching. It came quickly and hove to neatly a few yards from them.

Ralph looked up at the friendly faces of the sailors leaning over the rail above and knew that he was safe. It was a moment of huge relief, but he and the other boys were so weak that they had to be carried onto the destroyer, as did several of the Indians. On board he enjoyed the wonderful freedom of being able to stretch his legs without touching another body. He was given a seaman's sweater and a pair of socks, both many sizes too large.

That night Ralph was too tired to consider the implications of his rescue and slept deeply. In the morning, after experiencing the bliss of being able to eat, drink and wash, he learnt that Father John and the hallucinating boy were in the sickbay while one of the Indians had died. Later that day the destroyer steamed up the Firth of Clyde past the beautiful islands of Arran and Bute. For so long surrounded by sea, he found the green of grass and trees entrancing. They berthed at Gourock that evening and were put up at the town's best hotel.

Ralph, along with the other boys, had been met on landing by CORB representatives who had already telephoned his mother to inform her of his survival, and she was coming to Glasgow to meet him the next day. He learnt what had happened after the sinking. Of the ninety children on board only seven, apart from the six of them, had survived while six of the ten escorts had drowned. Miss Wood and the two girls were not among the survivors. Until news of their own rescue broke, it had been assumed that they too had perished.

Ralph, notwithstanding his joy at the prospect of seeing his mother so soon, was worried at the effect the shock of his presumed death and subsequent survival would have had on her. She must have been overwhelmed with emotions of despair, guilt, sorrow and eventually relief. Then she would have had to have a traumatic telephone conversation with her Canadian cousins informing them of the sinking. And her final words to him, 'Goodbye, darling, it won't be for long,' must now seem ironic.

He was not sure of the impact of the events during the same period on himself. He had changed. Having faced death for more than a week, he was aware, as never before, of the fragility of human life, particularly his own. Two of his contemporaries who had been with him at the start of the journey had died. In consequence, relief at his own survival was mixed with grief. He was conscious of the debt he owed to the crew of the lifeboat for keeping them afloat in terrible conditions. He was also deeply grateful to Kathy, who had lavished care and encouragement on him at a time when she, like the rest of them, must have been exhausted herself, and to Father John for leading them in prayer. Prayer had helped him when the outlook was bleak. And in adversity he had formed a bond with Ronnie, with whom he would keep in touch. He felt older but less confident. During the night, his first onshore, he dreamt that he was back in the lifeboat with the storm about to break and the cargo vessel steaming away from them. He was to be revisited by this nightmare many times. After waking up he immediately felt for the tumbler of water by his bedside. Fear of thirst was to remain with him too.

The next morning Kathy came to say goodbye to them. He felt very close to her, partly because of her kindness to him and partly because of the suffering they had shared. He knew that she must be deeply distressed to learn that only one of her original charges had survived—the others having died of cold in a waterlogged lifeboat during the twenty-four hours that elapsed before they were picked up by a destroyer. She kissed them all and said, 'We must keep in touch,' but Ralph knew it was unlikely that they would be able to do so. He felt guilty because the pain of parting from her outweighed the coming joy of seeing his mother again.

II

THE HOLY LAND

'Put your sword back, for all who draw the sword
will die by the sword'

Matthew Ch.26: 52-53

The night after his visit to Yad Vashem Ralph dreamt again of being in the lifeboat with the cargo ship steaming away from them. He awoke frightened. After all those years the memory of the sinking could still affect him. Being in extreme discomfort and danger of death for eight days and nights had scarred him. It had been difficult to talk to his mother—and later school friends—about it. Washed and wearing new clothes provided by CORB, he must have appeared to his mother much the same as when they parted and he had done his best to pretend that this was so, concealing the fear and insecurity that he felt. He did not wish to upset her, and he knew that it would be impossible to explain how he felt to her or others who had not shared his experience. He had longed to see Kathy again and to discuss it all with her, but school terms, the war and petrol rationing had prevented this.

It was still early and he tried unsuccessfully to get back to sleep. His mind was hyperactive, switching from past to present. Yesterday, while queuing to visit the Temple Mount, a young

Israeli woman dressed in black had come up to their group and told them that they must recognize that Judaea and Samaria had been given by God to the Jews, to whom they still belonged. The thought of God reminded Ralph that he was due to walk the Via Dolorosa that morning. After a self-service breakfast in the modern Grand Court Hotel, a bus took them to the city walls. It was a fine day.

As Ralph entered the Old City at St Stephen's Gate, the fruit in a stall to his left glowed orange, red and green in the sun. The route then narrowed and darkened with arches overhead. Passing the Apostle Peter's Prison, where gold on a doorway glittered, his party turned right up Al-Mujahideen Street to stop in a courtyard. A classical façade in honey-coloured stone confronted them. Tradesmen offered their wares, some small boys begged and a money changer advertised his services. Here Jesus had been condemned.

'Here' was in fact about twelve feet down, as buildings and pavements had over the centuries been built on top of the original route. Ralph tried to imagine the scene that cold, grey morning over two thousand years before. Dark clouds to the north-west presaged a storm as the Roman soldiers began escorting the prisoner from the Praetorium to the place of execution. They walked along a stone-paved street with buildings to either side. The prisoner was in a pitiful state. Weak with loss of blood and carrying a heavy cross, he fell several times. People jeered at him, though not everyone. One woman leant out and wiped the blood, sweat and spittle off his face with a cloth.

Monsignor Bob, who was leading the pilgrimage, reminded them that, when accused, Jesus 'opened not his mouth', and that in the Garden of Gethsemane he had refused to meet violence with violence, telling one of his supporters, 'Put your sword back, for all who draw the sword will die by the sword'. What a contrast, Ralph thought, with the tit-for-tat violence that had characterised events in this country since his first visit seventy years ago.

Turning left and emerging into sunshine Ralph's spirits rose. In his trainers the worn paving stones felt good to tread and faintly familiar.

★★★

Ralph was on a soft-foot patrol, which meant that his men wore rubber-soled shoes so they could move silently after dark over the paved streets and stone floors of buildings. Although it was barely two years since the end of the war and the release by the Allies of European Jews from concentration camps in Germany, the atmosphere in Jerusalem had become increasingly hostile to the British Army and the battalion had received information that arms might be hidden in the Armenian church.

As Ralph led his men into the building the smell of incense was all-pervading, and he realized that an evening service was in progress. They searched in the candlelight for hidden spaces in the walls but found nothing that night. He thought it odd for him, a Christian, to be warily leading his platoon with loaded rifles a few hundred yards from the Church of the Holy Sepulchre. But then perhaps it was not so strange since armed men had escorted Jesus to his execution along this very way— and, as it happened, a few days before he had been detailed to escort a visiting brigadier up the Via Dolorosa with an armed guard in front and behind them. He had then thought of the Roman soldier at Calvary responsible for carrying out the Crucifixion and controlling the crowd, who had suddenly found himself deeply moved by the man on the cross. Ralph's job was to watch the brigadier's back, but he could not prevent part of his mind switching to events of two thousand years ago. What impact had witnessing the Crucifixion made on that officer who, in the course of his military career, happened to be stationed in Jerusalem at that time? For that matter, he wondered, what impact would his posting to Palestine have on his own life?

Ralph had only been in the army for eight months. Called up in the summer of 1946, he had initially been posted to the Rifle Regiment near Winchester. He was the second person that afternoon to reach the barrack room, which was to be their home for the next twelve weeks' basic training. He and the other recruit—also, he discovered, from a private school—speculated on how the members of their platoon would get on with each other, coming as they did from widely varying backgrounds. He soon realized that he need not have worried, for their common fear of the army bonded them.

Ex-boarding school, Ralph found the experience less alarming than did those who had never been away from home before. However, he was conscious of being in the power of the army without parental support and it was up to him whether he sank or swam. A lot of their so-called free time was spent polishing boots and blancoing webbing, although this did provide an opportunity to talk and learn about each other's lives. By day they practised fieldcraft at Barton Stacey, carrying out recces, crawling through nettles and preparing platoon attacks in which it was important not to forget the bigger picture. They were fortunate in their platoon NCO, who by force of personality managed to maintain control without ever raising his voice, a rare attribute in the army at that time.

After a few weeks Ralph attended a War Office Selection Board. This involved problem solving outdoors, giving an impromptu talk, and showing some leadership skills, with which he knew he was not over-endowed. Somehow, he passed. This meant that, having completed his basic training, he went to the Officer Training School for the Infantry at Eaton Hall in

Cheshire. The course there lasted four months during which time he and his fellow officer cadets were kept under pressure and made to take charge of their platoon in turn so that their leadership potential could be assessed. Ralph got through but conditions were rugged. The winter of 1947 was one of the severest on record with snow on the ground from January to March.

Where people went after Eaton Hall depended on the regiment into which they were commissioned. Each officer cadet had three choices. Ralph's first choice was the Rifle Regiment. He got his second, the North Country Regiment, which recruited from around where his grandmother lived. However, perhaps because he had said on the army recruitment form that he was interested in the Middle East and Africa and knew a little Arabic, he found that he had been posted to Palestine on secondment to the Parachute Regiment, known as the Paras. His reactions to this were mixed. He felt proud to have been commissioned and to have been posted to a trouble spot, but at the same time worried about whether he would be able to cope and about his survival; a good number of British soldiers had been killed in Palestine over the previous two years. He was to join the 6th Airborne Division and his battalion was stationed in Jerusalem.

When Ralph received his travel instructions it was with slight apprehension that he read that he was to embark from Liverpool. This feeling revisited him a few days later as he crossed the gangway and stepped aboard the *Dunnotar Castle*. He was still feeling daunted at the prospect of going to Jerusalem where he knew nobody and would be expected to perform in a stressful situation. However, on his first night at sea he found a kindred spirit in the bar, a major in the Royal Engineers, who was returning to Palestine from leave. He had a weather-beaten look.

'In spite of its troubles, Palestine is a fascinating place to be posted to,' the major said. 'British officials working there during the Mandate used to say "there is no promotion from Palestine".' Apart from his acquaintance with and enthusiasm for Palestine, the major had been around, survived the war and was clearly undaunted by anything. By the end of the voyage some of his confidence had rubbed off on Ralph.

Thanks to the major the twelve-day voyage, on a relatively calm sea, proved a peaceful interlude for Ralph. He had brought a book about Palestine, intending to brief himself. He learnt that Balfour's Declaration of 1917, that the Jews had a historic claim to a home in their ancient land, had never been accepted by the Arabs who lived there. The book quoted George Kidston, a perceptive Foreign Office official writing in 1919, who pointed out that under Balfour's proposals Palestine would go to the Zionists irrespective of the wishes of the majority of the Arab population. Kidston commented that the idea that this programme would entail bloodshed and military repression never seemed to have occurred to Balfour. Twenty-eight years on, Ralph was about to be caught up in the bloodshed.

After disembarking at Port Said in mid-March, the troops travelled by train to Jerusalem; the guards at the station and on the train were carrying guns. He was met at the station in Jerusalem by a subaltern wearing the Paras' red beret, who said, 'Welcome to Jerusalem. I hope you had a peaceful journey.' As they were getting into a jeep, along with a soldier armed with a Sten gun, his brother officer told him that security was even tighter than usual on account of an attack on an officers' club in Jerusalem a fortnight before, in which thirteen British soldiers were killed. Moreover, only a day ago, four members of the Jewish Underground had been executed at Acre and reprisals were expected.

They drove to the Hospice de Notre Dame de France opposite New Gate where the Paras battalion was stationed. Unlike the formality and 'don't speak until you're spoken to' atmosphere of his parent regiment's officers' mess, to which he had briefly belonged before his departure, the mess in Jerusalem was relaxed. Ralph was greeted warmly by his fellow officers and introduced to his commanding officer and to Major MacDonald, who was to be his company commander.

Ralph found himself thrown in at the deep end. One thing that struck him at once was that, although the 6th Airborne Division had been sent out in late 1945 to fill the role of peacemaker between Arabs and Jews, his men were now hostile to the latter. And he soon realized why. They had started off feeling sympathy for the Jews on account of their sufferings in Europe during the war. One member of his platoon had even taken part in the liberation of Belsen. In 1940 Britain and her empire had stood alone against Hitler's forces so how, his men asked, could the Jews now turn against them? But, after being called Nazis and, contemptuously, red poppies on account of their berets and subjected to repeated terrorist attacks, their attitude had changed.

Broadcasts from the Jewish Underground, transcripts of which Major MacDonald gave Ralph to read, made clear that they saw Britain as the chief obstacle to their aim of forming a Jewish state, and they hoped that their terrorist attacks on British troops and police would encourage the British to depart. Hence in March 1946 seven Paras were killed by the Jewish Underground while guarding a car park in Tel Aviv. Four months later two of Ralph's brother officers told him that they had been on their way to a celebratory lunch at the King David Hotel—one of the great hotels of the Orient—which was then serving both as a hotel and as the British Military Headquarters in Palestine. Fortunately for them they never got there because, while they were still three hundred yards away, part of the hotel blew up killing twenty-eight British, forty-one Arabs and seventeen Jews.

Thus it was a tense situation in which Ralph found himself. He was kept busy liaising with the police over the possible location of illegal arms and organising searches of suspect vehicles or sites. One aspect, which he particularly disliked, was that when on a site being searched Jewish women often surrounded their men and had to be physically removed by the soldiers to get access to the men for questioning. The object of this tactic was to provide photographic evidence of 'British brutality'.

Soon after his arrival, while conducting a search, he found himself for the first time having to make safe a milk-churn bomb packed with gelignite, which had been left by the Underground in the hope of blowing up those looking for illicit arms. He knew how to do it but doing it for the first time with his platoon sergeant watching was nerve-racking.

Sporadic shooting took place all over the city at night. Listening to the reports echoing round the hills, Ralph was soon able to recognize the weapons being fired—usually rifles and Stens but with an occasional mortar. It was mostly caused by Jews and Arabs firing at each other. Ralph and the battalion officers rarely went out at night for social events. However, Ralph did sometimes go out on duty by jeep—there were always two vehicles—to pull down and collect Hebrew political posters put up by the Jewish Underground.

By the time Ralph arrived the lives of British soldiers had become restricted. They could only go out in groups of not less than four, and for much of the time were confined to barracks. If an officer ate out at a restaurant he was required to be armed. Ralph found that having a loaded revolver in his pocket did not make for a relaxed meal. Social life had also been curtailed as a result of the evacuation at the beginning of the year of all British wives and children. There were plenty of attractive Jewish girls, but British soldiers were warned that liaison with local women could prove lethal.

For romance, Ralph and other young singles had to fall back on books, films and their imaginations. He used to play his recording of Carousel, which he had brought out with him along with a gramophone, when he was feeling lonely. Somewhere there must be someone for him. The mess took out subscriptions to social magazines which he looked at with interest. Many girls were featured in them after becoming engaged. But he noted one who was in because she had achieved an exhibition to study English at Cambridge. Something about her expression stuck in his mind, partly perhaps because he would, he hoped, be going to the same university.

For Ralph, Palestine was the first time, since being sunk in the Atlantic in 1940, that he had found himself in danger—his mother had kept him out of London as much as possible during the war by arranging for them both to spend the school holidays with his grandmother in the north of England. During his military training he had learnt how to handle weapons, including charging sand-filled sacks with a bayonet and, to scare 'the enemy' by screaming as he approached the target. In-out-on guard—it had all seemed a bit of a joke and slightly embarrassing at the time. But now he was leading his men for real in a hostile environment and it was quite possible that someone would take a shot at him, though the knowledge that he was in charge and responsible for the safety of his men helped to take his mind off his own peril. This was a crucial difference between his present situation and that of 1940. Then his survival had depended entirely on the skill and courage of others. Now it depended largely on his own judgement. Although he did not feel he was cut out to be a soldier, he was determined to be as good a one as he could. And one positive factor which helped him cope with the stresses of Jerusalem was that he liked and respected his company commander.

Major MacDonald, tall and moustached, looked a typical

pre-war regular army officer. However, he was a perceptive person, well read and with many wavelengths, who could be relied on to remain calm whatever the circumstances. This was unsurprising since he had survived capture at Dunkirk, escaped from prison at Warburg, walked to the Dutch frontier and eventually made his way back to Britain through France and Spain. Later he was dropped back into France to help the Resistance. In prison camp he had used his time to learn Arabic from another prisoner.

Ralph, an only child who had lost his father early on, felt isolated sometimes and in need of advice. However, he found it difficult to ask for it, particularly from his contemporaries. Occasionally he met an older person he could talk to easily. He had been lucky with his schoolmasters, one at his prep school, to which he had returned after being torpedoed, and another, a history teacher at his public school, who had fired his imagination. He was again fortunate to have found himself working under Major Mac, as he was called.

Major Mac seemed to have an inner peace, perhaps deriving partly from his having been through so much already that the things that worried most people no longer seemed important to him. He was a Roman Catholic and went to Mass when he could, although he also attended the Anglican Church Parade along with his men on Sundays. He had a classless quality and was popular with all ranks, who felt they could relate to him.

One morning in early June Major Mac came into their office and said, 'I've got news. We're moving camp.' He paused. 'It's to the Haifa region, some miles from the port, and in country where the birdlife could be interesting.'

Ralph had mixed feelings. He would be sad to leave Jerusalem, which retained its fascination despite the tense atmosphere. However, a change of scene would be refreshing and the prospect of being able to move around more freely and even walk in the countryside was attractive. Moreover, the camp was not far from the historic port of Acre dominated by a fortress dating from the twelfth century, which had been home first to the Crusaders and later to the Ottomans. During the Mandate it was turned into a prison for both Jews and Arabs, and it currently held a number of members of the Jewish Underground.

The battalion travelled by road, via Nablus, Jenin and Haifa, to their new camp. Their convoy, made up mainly of three-tonners and jeeps mounted with machine guns, must have been an attractive target but, thanks to the reconnoitring and clearing of potential ambush sites, it got through without incident. Ralph and Major Mac travelled near the front of the convoy in a jeep.

Compared with the Hospice de Notre Dame de France Ralph found the camp, when they reached it, unprepossessing. Huts were provided for messes, stores and offices but sleeping accommodation was in tents, only some of which had concrete bases. A perimeter fence of high barbed wire surrounded the camp, which was sited in gently rolling sandy country dotted with acacia and thorn. The Judean hills could be seen in the distance. The ancient port of Acre and the Jewish settlement of Nahariya were only a few miles away, with Haifa farther off but still within range if the battalion's help was needed. Major Mac had told Ralph that it was vital to keep Haifa working since this was the port from which British soldiers and civilian administrators would have to be evacuated were the Mandate to be ended.

Soon after their arrival Ralph accompanied Major Mac to Haifa to discuss future operations. Ralph had a friend there, Ronnie, who had been sunk with him in 1940 and was the only person in Palestine he already knew. They had arranged to meet.

Ronnie too had suffered from nightmares after their Atlantic ordeal and they had kept in touch by Christmas card, meeting up occasionally for coffee in London when Ralph was on his way to or from school. Ronnie's last card had given news of his posting to Haifa in the Intelligence Corps. Despite his smart uniform, highly polished boots and lance corporal's stripe, Ronnie looked much the same, a larger version of the boy on board ship seven years ago. As before, he was full of information, seeming to know when Britain would be leaving Palestine, although no announcement had yet been made. His manner was as confident as ever. 'Come May, be ready to pack up. Meanwhile the locals will grab what they can. Try not to get caught in the middle,' he advised. 'And don't get left behind,' he added, 'or you'll find yourself up shit creek without a paddle.'

Ralph asked what life was like in Haifa.

'No girls,' Ronnie said sadly. 'Have to make do with drink and a weekly film. Ever tried Traffic Lights—brandy, avocat and crème de menthe in layers? Looks pretty in the glass!'

Ralph enjoyed seeing Ronnie, whose terrier-like qualities must have been an asset in the Intelligence Corps, and they agreed to try and meet again. Life was unfair, Ralph thought, for if Ronnie had received a better education he would have had a pip instead of a stripe.

Ralph soon found himself sent back to Haifa with his platoon to help deal with the problem of illegal European Jewish immigrants. The Jewish Agency in Palestine had demanded Britain admit a hundred thousand immigrants. The Arab community had violently opposed this. Britain had unsuccessfully sought a compromise. The outcome was that large numbers of immigrants were arriving illegally and Ralph and his men, along with others, were ordered to prevent them from landing.

This involved unloading them and transferring them to other ships. For Ralph and his men, faced with battered boats containing hundreds of bedraggled men, women and children, who had already experienced the rigours of an uncomfortable voyage and were desperate to reach Palestine, the prospect was daunting.

One afternoon he stood on the deck, close to the gangway, of what had once been a US coastal passenger ship plying between Baltimore and Maryland. He looked around him. The ship had been boarded at sea by the British navy and was looking the worse for wear—railings ripped off, life rafts loose and cables dangling from the high bridge. He watched his men frogmarch two male immigrants who had refused to leave the ship voluntarily. Behind them, coming of her own accord, was a girl who, notwithstanding the strain and discomfort of the voyage, looked beautiful and about the same age as himself. His instinct was to smile encouragingly at her but before he could do so she looked up at him with eyes so full of scorn and rage that he just looked away.

Ralph knew that he was adding to the miseries of people who had already suffered greatly. For them, watching Palestine's coastline gradually fade from view as they departed for Cyprus or back to Europe, must have been like his own experience in 1940 of seeing the steamer on which he had pinned all his hopes disappear over the horizon.

In early July Ralph was involved in a search for two British sergeants who had been kidnapped by the Jewish Underground. The Underground's objective was to obtain hostages to bargain with and save the lives of three of their members who were under sentence of death in Acre prison. The Paras were charged with undertaking searches in Nahariya and further afield. Ralph thought continually about the two sergeants. They must have felt trapped in their no doubt claustrophobic prison, conscious that at any moment they might be killed. Once again, he remembered his feeling of being trapped in the lifeboat as the storm approached and the steamer abandoned them. But at least then he was among friends, while these two sergeants were in the hands of people who hated everything they stood for and saw them simply as a means to an end.

In the event the searches were unsuccessful and the executions of the Underground members went ahead. The next day the bodies of the two sergeants were found hanging. It emerged that, in addition to the discomfort of their prison, it had been so small and airtight that they had had to turn on oxygen cylinders to keep the air breathable. When their captors made clear to them what their fate was to be, they probably wished they had not turned on the taps.

That evening Ralph went into the mess to find a heated discussion going on. News had just been received that elements in the British police had, in retaliation for the hanging of the sergeants, inflicted injuries on Jews in Tel Aviv resulting in five deaths. One of the majors, whom Ralph liked, was complaining that the whole handling of the situation by the administration was pitifully weak and only encouraged atrocities like the hanging of the sergeants. Another officer commented, 'Force is the only thing that will stop them.' Ralph, horrified at what had happened to two young national servicemen, his own contemporaries, found himself agreeing with them. However, he noted that Major Mac had not joined in these critical comments, and in their office next morning asked him what he thought.

'Our government's in a tricky position. We can't find a compromise acceptable to both Arabs and Jews. While America is pressing us hard to allow more Jewish immigrants in, at home the public are getting increasingly angry at continued British casualties.'

By way of an afterthought Major Mac added, 'As for the hangings and what happened last night in Tel Aviv, I think it was unwise to have gone ahead with the executions at Acre. Violence breeds violence.'

Ralph found the atmosphere very tense in the aftermath of the hanging of the two sergeants, but after a few weeks it had relaxed enough for parties of soldiers to recommence visiting a beach near Nahariya, though always with an armed guard.

Accompanying the bathing parties gave Major Mac and Ralph an opportunity for birdwatching. Ralph also photographed birds and Palestine, as a crossroads for migrating birds, was an ideal place to do so. Songbirds, tired after crossing the Sahara, often took a break there and could be easily approached. The land directly behind the beach comprised sandy dunes and scrub, while nearer to Nahariya there were palm trees and, on the outskirts of the village, flower gardens which were home to the Palestine sunbird and many turtle doves.

One afternoon Ralph had come with a bathing party and, having posted pickets and intending not to stray too far from them, set off into the country behind the beach. As always outside the camp he was armed with a loaded revolver. That day he also carried his camera.

Ralph had barely gone fifty yards before he spotted to his left a yellow-vented bulbul flying a short distance towards Nahariya. Its black hood and long tail made it easy to recognize and he followed it slowly, hoping to get close enough for a photograph. Annoyingly, each time he thought he had got within range, it took off on another short flight, with the result that he was further from the pickets than he had intended.

Ralph was getting close to the outskirts of Nahariya when his single-minded pursuit of the bulbul was interrupted by the sound of gunfire behind him. He took his revolver out of its holster and ran to the top of the nearest dune to see what was happening. Coming fast along a track that would pass fifty yards or so from where he was standing was what looked like a British military vehicle. As it got closer he could see that in the back were some armed men in uniform. Assuming that they were British soldiers, he waved to attract their attention.

The next thing he knew, he was on the ground. It felt as if he had been hit hard by a cricket bat in his right shoulder. As he tried to pick himself up, he saw the vehicle continuing on its way. He touched his shoulder with his left hand. It felt wet and his right arm was limp. Managing to get to his feet, he felt unsteady but he could walk. Which way? The bathing party was half a mile distant while the nearest building in Nahariya was a bare hundred yards away. Given his condition, he knew he had to opt for the latter, although he remembered cases in Jerusalem where wounded British soldiers lying in the street had been ignored by Jewish passers-by.

Whether as a result of shock or loss of blood he found that he could only make slow progress over the sandy soil, and by the time he reached what turned out to be a bungalow he was exhausted. He knocked on the door. It was opened by an elderly lady who looked at his dishevelled appearance and blood-soaked khaki shirt with alarm. After hesitating for a moment, she signed to him to enter.

Inside, off a tiny hall, was a sitting room where she led him. Pointing to a chair she left the room. Ralph felt very faint but better for sitting down. He glanced round the tidy room and up at the framed photographs of elegantly dressed nineteenth-century figures, the woman's forebears no doubt. Outside he could hear a man and a woman talking in German and he remembered that this little port had originally been settled by German Jews. He had taken French and German in the Higher Certificate at school and could understand what they were saying.

The female voice was clearly that of the lady who had opened the door. The male voice, also elderly, probably that of her husband, was saying, 'The British are our enemies. It is not up to us to help him.'

The lady replied, 'We can't turn away a wounded man from our door. The Torah tells us to show mercy.'

Moments later the lady returned to the room with bandages. She was followed by a tense-looking elderly man who said questioningly to Ralph in English, 'My wife says you are hurt.'

'I've been shot in the shoulder,' Ralph replied.

'What are you doing here?' he asked in a hostile tone.

44

Since Ralph was armed and wearing uniform he could only say, 'I am a British soldier.'

'The British are preventing Jews from reaching their homeland,' the man continued accusingly.

'He is young and has to do what he is told,' the elderly lady interjected in German. She undid the buttons on Ralph's shirt. 'The bullet has made a furrow through the flesh, so it would be difficult to stitch,' she said. 'You have lost some blood so I will put a pressure pad on the wound to stop the bleeding.' She expertly set about bandaging his upper arm. 'You are lucky. Many years ago I trained as a nurse,' she said in a kindly voice. When she had finished she said, 'You will need to go to a hospital as soon as you can for an anti-tetanus inoculation and to have the shoulder examined and X-rayed. You may also need a blood transfusion,' she added. She then offered to telephone his superiors. As it happened, this was not necessary, for almost at once a jeep, which had been with the bathing party, came looking for him in Nahariya among the houses closest to where the party had been swimming.

Ralph heard subsequently that there had been a breakout from the ancient fortress prison at Acre and numerous Arab and Jewish prisoners had escaped. The breakout was organised by the Jewish Underground which had used stolen British military vehicles and operatives dressed in British military uniforms. Those who had fired on Ralph were members of the Underground and escaped Jewish prisoners who had been armed by their liberators. They had not expected to encounter British forces down by the sea and before firing at Ralph they had fired at his pickets who had also tried to wave them down.

After being shot, and while in hospital in Haifa before being sent home on sick leave, Ralph was visited by both his commanding officer and Major Mac. The former sympathised with him and thanked him for his service with the battalion. Major

Mac thanked him for his help and they exchanged addresses and agreed to keep in touch, in case he did not return to Palestine for what remained of his service. Ronnie also came to see him in hospital and congratulated him on having 'landed a cushy number'.

The doctor at the hospital told Ralph that his wound had done no permanent damage, apart from leaving a sizeable scar, but at the time it had bled profusely and if he had lost much more blood his life would have been in danger. Ralph reflected that he owed a lot to the elderly lady who, notwithstanding her husband's reluctance, had taken him in and bandaged his shoulder. As it was, he had quickly recovered after receiving blood transfusions in hospital.

As he travelled home, this time pleasurably, by train to Port Said, boat to Marseille, train across France and boat across the Channel, Ralph felt fortunate to have escaped so lightly. It was the second time he had been spared. The two young sergeants—he would always remember searching for them—and other contemporaries had not been so lucky. His experiences in Palestine, like those in the Atlantic, had underlined the fragility of human life and shown him how the moral choices of one individual can affect the life of another like his own that afternoon in Nahariya.

Ralph had indeed been caught up in the bloodshed foreseen by George Kidston in 1919 when commenting on the Balfour Declaration. He had witnessed the seemingly insoluble conflict between two peoples unfold and he had been the target of hatred and the recipient of mercy. He had come away convinced that, in the words of Major Mac, 'violence breeds violence'.

Ralph was conscious that Britain's exit from Palestine had been messy and undignified. Cracks were already appearing in the foundations of her huge empire. However, alive, aged twenty, and about to go to Cambridge, he was not too concerned about this.

III

CITY OF PEACE

'The sun shines in my city
The bells ring out for the heroes
Awake my beloved, we are free.'

Abdul Wahab Batati,
poem to commemorate the Revolution
in Iraq of 14 July 1958

Ralph went up to Cambridge in the autumn. It was a little over two years since he had joined the army. After his sick leave he had completed the remaining two months of his military service in England.

He had been to Cambridge once before for an interview by four daunting dons who had asked him to comment on the significance of symbols such as the alma mater. Coming straight from the barrack room, Cambridge had appeared magical. Happy people wearing gowns going to lectures, some beautiful girls among them, seemed from a different planet to his own, one of early rising, polishing, parades and strict discipline. Coming from Palestine, Cambridge's spell was unbroken. Apart from the relief of relaxing without fear of being shot or blown up, it was wonderful to be free and studying history again. However, having survived being sunk in the Atlantic and shot in Palestine, he did not wish to fritter his life away.

47

He still intended to try for the Foreign Service but knew the competition was intense and that he might well not get in. He also wanted to meet women. Having gone straight from a single-sex boarding school, with holidays in the remote countryside during petrol rationing, to military service in Palestine, he had hitherto had little opportunity.

He first recognized Mary, the girl whose image in a magazine had impressed him in Palestine, in the changeover time between lectures. Slim with dark hair framing a beautifully proportioned face, she seemed to glide through the throng, serene and unconscious either of her own looks or the glances of men. She did not attend any of Ralph's lectures and he remembered that she had come up to read English. He could see no way of meeting her and, given the preponderance of men to women at Cambridge and his own lack of sophistication, little chance of attracting her interest if he did.

During his first long vacation, however, he was invited to a dance in London and at the preceding dinner party found to his astonishment and delight that Mary was sitting at the same table as himself. He never got a chance to dance with her that evening but, on the basis of their both being at Cambridge, he found out her name and college, and asked if he could see her again in the autumn term.

Back in Cambridge he took his courage in both hands and invited her to tea, which seemed unthreatening for a first date. His digs were on the second floor of a little terraced house in a street some way from his college. They consisted of a bedroom and a sitting room-cum-study heated by a gas fire. Having invited her the week before he was increasingly excited as the day of Mary's visit approached. It turned out to be a wet afternoon and he was worried that she would not turn up. However, she did, despite the rain, damp and a little out of breath. As he helped her off with her coat, he caught a faint smell of scent mixed in with that of wet clothes. She sat down on the floor close to the fire with her legs tucked up under her. He could not remember what they talked about while sipping tea and toasting crumpets, but he found it exhilarating just to be alone with her in his room. In conversation the serenity he had noticed among the crowds of undergraduates was replaced by an enchanting, slightly mischievous smile. It was the first time he had ever entertained a girl to whom he was attracted in this way.

A few days later, after an invitation to a return-tea, he was bicycling out to Mary's college, some two miles from the centre of the city. She had told him to allow twenty minutes to get there, and nervous and anxious not to be late, he arrived five minutes early. This gave him time to take in the imposing red-brick Victorian building and its annexes set among cut grass, trees and flower beds.

He left his bicycle outside the Porter's Lodge and walked through the main entrance. No one challenged him so, obeying Mary's instructions, he mounted the stairs to the second floor where her room was. It was only when she opened the door and smiled that he began to relax. While she was out making the tea, he looked round. A sash window let in lots of light and looked out onto open country. Two prints of the Lake District hung from the picture rail and he noticed a record player on a table with a stack of records underneath.

They had talked about their common love of the Lake District, where it turned out they had both spent holidays, and then about their courses of studies and aspirations after university—she was interested in publishing. He had remarked on her collection of records, and she had asked him whether he would like to hear some. He nodded and said, "You choose". She put on first a beautiful Beethoven piano sonata which he knew, and then to his surprise and pleasure the record of Carousel— the best of the American musicals to have crossed the Atlantic after the war—which he had played so often in Palestine. While listening to the music their eyes met for an instant and he was conscious, as he had been in his own lodgings a few days before, of a spark between them.

Later that term Ralph took Mary to his Cambridge club's annual dance. However, it was difficult for their relationship to develop. Cambridge colleges were single-sex and there were then only two women's ones. Attractive girls were thus at a premium receiving lots of invitations. Even if he and Mary had been determined, they would have found it hard to conduct their social life as a couple. As it was, they had both led rather restricted lives up till then and relished their independence.

Ralph got a good enough degree to qualify for the Foreign Service but did not succeed in the competition. However, he was still keen to get into government service, as were many of his contemporaries in the aftermath of the war. And there was a chance of getting into the Foreign Service as a late entrant. After travelling and working abroad for two years post-Cambridge, and with this in mind, he in 1955 obtained an unestablished job with the Overseas Development Administration, which came under the Foreign Office at that time.

Mary and Ralph started to meet again in London. It was just after the Suez Crisis of 1956 and he was busy promoting Britain's aid effort to counteract the damage done to her prestige. He sensed that there was an opportunity for greater commitment on both their parts. However, the revival of their relationship was interrupted a little over a year later when the Overseas Development Administration offered him an eighteen-month posting to Beirut to work in the Middle East Development Division as an aid attaché. After much agonizing he accepted. At one level he was setting off on an exciting new venture. At another, perhaps deeper level, he was running away. He had let his relationship with Mary drift. He knew that he should have discussed it with her. What held him back? Fear of commitment and inhibition of revealing his emotions, a legacy from childhood.

Ralph returned to the Middle East in early 1958, this time by British Airways instead of troopship. He found Beirut enchanting. Bougainvillaea and hibiscus abounded. He was allocated a flat in a little hotel in Rue Agrippa. The sitting room looked across the bay to mountains sloping down to the sea. The coffee and croissants were fresh. It took only five minutes to walk to his office in the Middle East Development Division which sheltered under the wing of the British Embassy in the Avenue de Paris.

His boss was a blunt Yorkshireman, an agriculturalist with a dry sense of humour and a contempt for bureaucrats, whom he described as 'men of files'. The embassy staff were friendly and invited him to their parties. One shortly after his arrival was given by his own and other secretaries and had a twenties theme. It started with the Charleston and ended up with rock and roll. The latter was new to him and made him realize that, approaching thirty, he was no longer the younger generation. Most colleagues of his age were married while other singles were younger.

He found himself thinking about Mary. Being out of reach of her, he felt her absence the more. Although he liked Beirut, he could not help comparing his life as it was with what it might have been like had she been with him. He had forgotten how much he looked forward to taking her out and what a gap her absence left in his life. Going to parties would have been more enjoyable with her, entering a crowded room less daunting and talking about things afterwards fun. He remembered too her way with people and how, seemingly without trying, she could chat naturally and amusingly with anyone she met in a way he could never match. Nevertheless, Beirut was a pleasant place. He went riding over sand dunes by the airport and skied up at the Cedars. His new car arrived from England and he was able to drive with friends along the coast through Byblos to Tripoli. Time passed pleasantly enough but, as before when abroad, Ralph looked forward greatly to receiving twice-weekly airmail from England. He and Mary corresponded regularly, and he particularly enjoyed getting her letters giving news of mutual friends, her editorial work for a magazine and concerts she had been to in London. In return he sent her accounts of his life in Beirut. Their letters were warm and friendly without being over-emotional. But being away from England and other old friends he began to count on them more.

After a few months had passed Ralph's boss decided that he should visit Jordan and Iraq, make contact with some of the beneficiaries of British aid there and write some pieces showing ways in which Britain was helping the area. The Middle East Development Division's main interests were outside Lebanon and its object was the encouragement of small businesses and farmers, particularly in territories formerly under British administration.

Accordingly, that July afternoon, Ralph was back in Jerusalem, looking down on an ugly scar made up of barbed wire and concrete, which snaked across the divided city. Ten years had passed since he had acquired his own scar. Meanwhile, the war between Arabs and Jews that followed in May 1948 had ended up with Israeli forces in control of West Jerusalem and Transjordanian forces in control of the Old City. They had signed an armistice in April 1949 and, despite the United Nations General Assembly having in December 1949 voted in favour of Jerusalem becoming an international city under UN administration, neither of them had shown any inclination to relax their grip. While there was tension at times and sniping along the border between them, both powers were agreed on opposing internationalization. Since no country was prepared to provide soldiers to evict them by force, and after the Soviet

Union had in 1950 broken ranks by formally withdrawing its support for internationalization, the rest of the international community had gradually during the 1950s moved towards accepting the de facto situation without formally recognizing it.

For Ralph in 1958 the Old City, now under Jordanian control, was a lot safer than he remembered it. He could eat out unarmed and walk up the Via Dolorosa without fear of being shot in the back. He had done so with no trouble other than the unsolicited attentions of a persistent Palestinian would-be tourist guide in search of a tip.

After looking at a light industry project in the Old City which the Development Division had supported, Ralph repaired to the American Colony Hotel where he was to spend the night. Dining alone in the hotel's trellised courtyard he wondered what had happened to the elderly lady from Nahariya who had treated his shoulder. However, given the present political and security situation, there was no way in which he could cross into Israel to find out.

Next morning, he met up with a car and driver from the British Embassy who had to visit Jerusalem on business and had agreed to give him a lift back to Amman. On the way they stopped to see some irrigation and terracing projects close to the River Jordan, equipment for which had been supplied by the Development Division. These seemed to be working well.

Ralph directed his driver to a site near the Jordan where he was to have lunch with a group of farmers. He found them sitting cross-legged in a circle. Soon he was served with a huge plateful of charcoal-grilled chicken. It was tender and delicious. Ralph's neighbours, both elderly, were courteous but after the meal they told him they felt betrayed by the British Government. It was the British, they said, who had given the Jews the opportunity of creating the State of Israel and led to their being deprived of their land. And now, they complained, neither the UN nor the Great Powers would do anything to remedy this injustice. Ralph

53

decided that the best response was to listen sympathetically and praise what they had achieved in building terraces on inhospitable hillsides and installing irrigation projects. They had indeed done a remarkable job.

After lunch Ralph walked back from the picnic site to the road as the diesel engine pump, which his division had supplied, belched intermittently in the background. These Palestinian farmers, he thought, while personally friendly to him, would never forgive Britain for the loss of their land.

Ralph's car soon crossed the Allenby Bridge over the Jordan river and sped on its way to Amman where he was to stay the night before going on to Iraq the next day. He spent an enjoyable evening in Amman with a friend, now the First Secretary, who told him that both Jordan and Iraq were being attacked daily by Cairo Radio for being 'imperialist stooges'. It was hard to know what damage these tirades were doing to the two Hashemite kingdoms. He called in at the embassy the next morning to report on his meetings in Jerusalem and with the West Bank Palestinian farmers. While he was there one of the secretaries asked him if he could take a birthday card to a member of the Diplomatic Wireless Service at the British Embassy in Baghdad. He agreed to do so and caught a late-morning flight on there on Friday 11 July.

In the plane he thought about his conversation with his friend the evening before. Hussein and Feisal, first cousins and Kings of Jordan and Iraq, were both only twenty-three, seven years younger than himself, but were already loaded with frightening responsibilities. Like him they had lost their fathers young—Feisal when he was four, while Hussein, aged sixteen, had been present at his father's assassination. Now, apparently, disaffections in the Jordanian army had led to the arrest of some officers. This had alarmed Hussein who had asked Feisal to send reinforcements.

Ralph had deliberately arranged to arrive in Baghdad on a Friday so he would have the weekend in which to meet up with two old friends. One was Ronnie, who had decided to stay in the army and, after a spell in the UK, had been posted to Hong Kong and on to Korea when war began there in 1950. At present he was stationed in Habbaniya, the remaining British base in Iraq. The other was Major Mac, now a brigadier, who had been appointed a senior British representative on the Baghdad Pact, a defensive alliance against the Communist threat. Major Mac had kindly offered to put Ralph up. His wife had gone on mid-tour leave and he was to follow her shortly.

Ralph felt he was stepping into an oven as he got out of the plane at Baghdad mid-afternoon. Emerging from the airport building he spotted a man holding a notice reading 'Brigadier MacDonald's driver'. Ralph had never been to Baghdad before but had a romantic idea of it based on having read *The Arabian Nights* and *Sinbad the Sailor* as a child. He had also done some background reading and had noted that the Caliph Mansur, who had founded Baghdad in 762, had named it Madinat al-Salaam, the City of Peace. After a brilliant start it had been downhill all the way. Low spots included Hulagu's sacking of it in 1258, three hundred years as a backwater of the Ottoman Empire, and capture by the British General Maude in 1917. Although Britain's Mandate of Iraq expired and the country became independent in 1932, British influence had remained strong with the military base at Habbaniya and the presence of economic experts.

Ralph's own interest was in the economy, which seemed to be working quite well thanks to the receipt of oil revenues. And, although conditions in Iraq were far from perfect, Ralph thought they compared very favourably with those in other Middle Eastern countries at the time.

The road from the airport ran through flat brown dried-up land containing a few dilapidated buildings and the chassis of abandoned vehicles. However, it did not take long to reach Mansur, a suburb on the same side of the Tigris as the airport, but in sharp contrast made up of bungalows with neat well-watered gardens. Major Mac's bungalow was on the edge of the town and backed on to the desert which, barring some irrigated land, surrounded the city. The driver dropped Ralph there and then went off to collect Major Mac from his office.

Ralph was offered a cup of tea by the cook but said that he would prefer to wait. He looked round the sitting room. There were photographs of a boy and a girl, a watercolour of an eighteenth-century house with hills in the background, and a striking bronze head of a young woman. Ralph was reminded that Major Mac, as a young officer, had met his future wife in France at the beginning of the war and that, despite not seeing each other for five years, they had remained true to each other and married soon after the war ended.

Half an hour later, Ralph heard the car crunch on the gravel outside the front door and Major Mac appeared, suntanned and a little thinner about the face but otherwise much the same as before. Ralph, after congratulating him on his appointment and promotion, asked after his family, saying that he was sorry to miss seeing his wife again. She had been evacuated by the time he reached Jerusalem in 1947. Major Mac said that he was soon going on leave, but in view of the heat and the situation in the country he had encouraged his wife to go on ahead of him.

Surprised at Major Mac's concern about the situation, Ralph asked, 'With a popular young king and oil revenues coming in, Iraq looks to be doing alright?'

'Looks can be deceptive,' Major Mac replied. 'In the Baghdad Pact I work with Iranians and Turks, who keep their ears close to the ground and are worried about what they hear. I'm worried too. My instinct tells me something is wrong.'

After supper they talked again about the political situation.

Major Mac's view was that while the top people in the Iraqi army and government were pro-Western and supported the monarchy, many middle-ranking officers and government officials had been influenced by Cairo Radio and made to feel that their government was out of tune with Arab nationalism and in the pocket of the West. He felt that there was a lot of discontent in the country which could flare up at any time.

The next morning Major Mac agreed to drive Ralph to the British base at Habbaniya so that he could see Ronnie. They set off at 7 a.m. to avoid the worst of the heat. Habbaniya was about seventy miles away and the road passed through Falluja before reaching Habbaniya Lake, filled with water from the Euphrates, where they planned to stop for a swim. Although the sun had been on the shallows for several hours the water was still cool enough to be refreshing. They reached the camp at lunchtime. It was neat and tidy with painted white stones marking the entrance, like British military camps the world over, and home to a few hundred British servicemen, mostly RAF. Major Mac wanted to visit the NAAFI to buy baked beans, Marmite, cornflakes, and other items unobtainable in Baghdad. He also had to see a friend in the camp, so Ralph had arranged to meet Ronnie on his own in the camp's pub, which sold draught beer.

The pub had a noisy but effective air cooler and it was a relief to get out of the sun. Ronnie, who was already waiting, was wearing khaki shorts and a bush jacket. Ralph saw the crown on his sleeve. Coming up through the ranks, he had done very well to have been promoted to warrant officer in eleven years. His uniform looked strange to Ralph, used to lightweight suits and flowing robes, but it was in keeping with this little patch of England in the desert. They looked at each other and shook hands.

Ronnie had been in Iraq for six months and had another six to go.

'Well, how are things?' Ralph asked.

'Pleasant enough,' Ronnie replied. 'Compared with Korea this place is one long holiday camp. It's hot in the middle of the day but one can cool off in here or go for a swim. In the Korean winter we were always cold and there was no way to warm up. It rained and snowed a lot but there was never enough water to wash with. I only ever got a bath thanks to the kindness of my American opposite number. It got quite hairy too—the Chinese would come on at us however many casualties they took. And when we got home, instead of being welcomed we got given a hard time from Customs, looking for drugs.'

The camp was entirely staffed by British personnel. Ronnie's job involved routine liaison with the Iraqi army in Falluja over administrative matters. His visits there were mainly made out of courtesy, to keep the Iraqis informed of events which they might consider they ought to know about. Ronnie, with his flair for getting on with people, had made close friends with his Iraqi contact. Over numerous tiny cups of tea, he had gained the impression that a good many middle-ranking and some senior officers did not have much love for Britain which, post-Suez, was seen as a spent force. President Nasser, on the other hand, was much admired by them. Ralph greatly enjoyed seeing Ronnie again. Apart from his dry sense of humour, they were bonded by their common experience in the Atlantic. And despite his jokey manner, he was a shrewd observer.

On the way back to Baghdad Ralph told Major Mac of Ronnie's take on the Iraqi army. Major Mac expressed no surprise. It fitted in with his own impressions. However, he was also sure that a few of the most senior Iraqi officers could be relied on to remain loyal to the monarchy, Britain and the West. In a crisis it would all depend on who initially seized control.

They were both tired by the time they got back to Mansur. Major Mac, who knew of Ralph's love of horses, had arranged for them to go riding the next afternoon. In the morning Ralph decided to accompany Major Mac to Mass at the Catholic Church since the Anglican service at St George's was at a different time. The congregation constituted a mix of expatriates and Iraqi Christians. Ralph found it a moving service. In Iraq, then as in the time of the Abbasid Caliphs, people were free to practise their religion and there was no ill feeling towards Christians, who had been there since the time of the Apostles.

After they had had a rest and a cup of tea, the groom came to the back of the bungalow riding one horse and leading another. Both horses were Arabs of about fifteen hands and had started life on the racetrack but had not proved fast enough. The air was getting cooler as they rode out into the desert, which was red and hard, full of ridges and dry stream beds. It was peaceful with no other people about. The landscape, so harsh and glaring by day, turned to soft shades of ochre as the sun sank lower. Sound carried and from afar Ralph could hear the creaking of a cart. They saw no animals save for two jackals which ran away. The horses pricked up their ears at the sight of them. Later they put up a pair of sand grouse.

That evening Ralph read up his notes on agriculture in preparation for the meeting he was to have with the First Secretary (Aid) in the morning. Iraq's development plan was sound in that oil revenues were being reinvested in industries and agriculture. However, these were mostly long-term projects like dams. The downside was that agricultural reforms were needed quickly to improve the lives of the lowly paid and often exploited farm workers. Many of these had gravitated towards Baghdad only to find that there were no jobs available and that they had had to eke out an existence in the slums surrounding the city, doing temporary work when they could get it. The government was conscious of these problems but could be criticised for not tackling them with sufficient energy. Consequently, some sectors of

Iraqi society nursed grievances and were looking for someone to blame. Ralph thought he could issue warnings and encourage remedial action tactfully, though whether anyone would do anything about it was another matter.

Office hours at the British Embassy in Baghdad were 7 a.m. to 1.30 p.m. so Ralph had set his alarm clock for 5.45. Lying in bed for a few moments after it had gone off, he heard the sound of gunfire. It was probably training on a nearby range in the cool of the early morning, he thought.

Then Major Mac knocked on his door and opened it. 'Baghdad Radio has just announced that there has been a military coup,' he said. 'We had better get you to the embassy and me to my office as soon as possible.' They dressed rapidly and after a hasty cup of tea and slice of toast set off in Major Mac's own car, there being no sign of his driver.

As soon as they reached Damascus Street, the main road leading towards the river and the embassy, they noticed some armoured cars parked at the roadside. Many people on foot, including the odd soldier, were moving up the road towards the city centre, some of them at the run. The Iraqis mostly ignored their car with its CD plates until, arriving at the railway line, a few of them looked unfriendly and barred their way. Major Mac greeted them with a smile and courteously explained in Arabic that he needed to get to his office. They were allowed to pass.

The embassy was situated on the west bank of the Tigris away from other embassies in the old and poorer part of the city called Karkh. Arriving at its iron gates, they found a small crowd of people. Initially hostile, they again became less so after being greeted by Major Mac. He dropped Ralph off and was allowed to continue on his way to the Baghdad Pact offices. Ralph looked up at the equestrian statue of General Maude, the British conqueror of Baghdad in 1917. The General and his horse stood outside the gates on an imposing white stone pedestal, gazing out into the distance. His presence there could hardly be more provocative, Ralph thought.

The guard on the gate let Ralph through and he walked up the drive towards the embassy, an elegant building made of yellow brick in Ottoman style. Another guard let Ralph through the outer door of the embassy building and he found himself in a courtyard. The building was on two floors and a balcony facing inwards, supported by slender columns, surrounded the upper floor which had offices leading off it, while high exterior walls provided protection.

Ralph was directed to the Head of Chancery's office. His door was open and he was listening to a radio on his desk. He glanced up as Ralph came in and said with a rueful smile, 'Welcome, I'm sorry about this.' He was about the same age as Ralph, and his calm voice, tidy appearance and pipe gave an impression of dependability.

'I'm sorry too,' Ralph replied. 'Visitors must be the last thing you want right now'. Ralph was told that the assassination of the crown prince had just been announced and that the embassy's own position was unsafe since the coup was anti-British as well as anti-monarchical. If the situation became more threatening, the plan was for the embassy staff to forgather in the Registry, which was on the ground floor down some steps and protected by a steel grille. In the meantime, Ralph could remain in his office and listen to the radio.

There was a lot of conflicting news and it was difficult to get a clear picture. Broadcasts from Turkey, Iraq and Jordan reported that the Iraqi 2nd Army was loyal to the king and coming to Baghdad from Kirkuk and Arbil. The BBC World Service quoted Baghdad Radio as saying that the crown prince had been assassinated but that Nuri al-Said, the Federal Prime Minister, had escaped and that there was a reward of 10,000 dinars on his head.

Ralph remembered that he had a letter to deliver to one of the Diplomatic Wireless Service staff and was directed to their office on the upper floor. Handing over the letter he did not stop to talk as the addressee was busy transmitting. On his way back, before descending the stairs, he exchanged smiles with an elderly man leaning over the balcony opposite. Back on the ground floor the shouts from the crowd seemed to be getting closer so he made his way to the Registry, which was already quite full.

It was now nearly eleven and the guards on the embassy gates reported that they were under increasing pressure from the mob, which had grown in size and had already toppled the statue of General Maude. A few minutes later it was reported that the gates had given way and the rioters had entered the embassy compound. As the embassy building was protected by locks and grilles, the mob, it appeared, were focusing on the Ambassador's Residence which stood nearby. Those in the Registry could smell burning and see smoke. Soon, however, it was the embassy's turn with rioters appearing in the central courtyard and looting the contents of offices. It was afterwards discovered that they had gained access by pulling out some of the bars on the exterior windows of the building where the plaster holding them had deteriorated over the years.

Some of the rioters had rifles which they were firing indiscriminately into the air. At this point a message was received from the second floor that an attaché had been killed. Without needing to be told, Ralph knew this must be the elderly man who had smiled at him a few minutes before.

The Registry, a long narrow room lit by artificial light and somewhat claustrophobic at the best of times, was now sheltering about fifty people ranging from the ambassador and his wife to young secretaries, and including both UK and locally based staff. Although protected by the grille, their position was precarious. Ralph could hear one of the embassy's Arab speakers talking to the rioters through the grille. The latter were demanding access to the Registry where they believed arms were being hidden. Failure to comply would result in staff being smoked out. Some lighted paper and a can of petrol were produced to reinforce the point. It was a bad moment but inside everyone preserved a calm front, whatever their feelings may have been. At risk in a confined space with others, Ralph found his mind flashing back to being on the boat crowded with sailors and evacuees in 1940. He thought of Mary. If he got out of this situation he would write her a different sort of letter on his return to Beirut.

The ambassador decided to risk being lynched outside the Registry rather than roasted inside. The staff formed a scrum with the girls in the middle and the men on the outside, and made their way slowly out through the screaming, spitting mob, towards the ambassador's lawn. Those on the outside were roughed up and some had their watches and wallets stolen but did not come to serious harm. For a moment Ralph caught the eyes of one of those harassing them. They were wild and uncommunicative. The British group had been demonised. He had been hated before and he remembered the look the Jewish girl had given him in Haifa docks when he was unloading illegal immigrants from a ship in 1947.

On the lawn they found Iraqi tanks in situ but making no attempt to save the smouldering residence or to control the rioters. Rather they turned their guns inwards, pointing them at the bedraggled group of embassy staff as if it were they who presented the threat.

Ralph felt his pocket. His wallet was still there and his watch remained on his wrist. He had been lucky, he thought, as he wiped the spittle off his face and jacket. However, it was very hot and he could feel the sweat trickling down his back. They were without shelter or water for several hours. Again, both thirst and what seemed a long wait for rescue reminded him of 1940. Eventually a senior Iraqi officer turned up and told the tanks to withdraw.

Most of the cars in the embassy's car park had been set on fire so the Iraqi military, who at last did something helpful, took the ambassador and his wife and other staff, including Ralph, to the Baghdad Hotel. Major Mac joined them there later, the Baghdad Pact offices having come to no harm. They decided to spend the night at the hotel rather than risk driving back to Mansur with rioters still out on the streets. The next day, however, they considered it safe to return there, Major Mac having kindly invited Ralph to remain at his bungalow until flights out of Baghdad Airport resumed.

That evening they sat on the flat roof of the bungalow. The stars were bright and seemed very close. The air was warm and a caressing breeze from the desert blew the smoke from their cigarettes away, while the lights of the town twinkled all around and the music from radios in neighbouring sarifas sounded friendly. It was hard to believe that the violent acts of the previous day had taken place.

Major Mac poured Ralph a generous whisky saying, 'You deserve this. You must have had a worrying time in the Registry.'

Ralph was longing for a drink and an opportunity to talk about the events of the last thirty-six hours. 'Yes, especially when a chap with a can of petrol started pushing a piece of lighted paper under the grille. I didn't think he'd pour the petrol on, but you couldn't be sure.'

'How did the staff react?'

'Everyone put on a brave face whatever they may have been feeling. It was hard on the ambassador who had to decide what to do.' Knowing that one of his staff had been killed and that his house and his possessions had almost certainly gone up in flames, Ralph thought the ambassador had shown great courage.

'Was the attaché shot by accident?'

Ralph remembered the kindly looking man smiling at him on the balcony. It was difficult to take in that he was dead. 'No one knows. There was chaos going on in the courtyard with shots being fired in the air, so it could have been an accident. Equally, he could have been shot deliberately by someone intent on causing maximum damage to Anglo-Iraqi relations.'

Since they had set off from the bungalow on the morning of 14 July, it had emerged that in addition to the crown prince, the rebel soldiers had killed several princesses and mortally wounded the king who had subsequently died.

Topping up Ralph's glass, Major Mac said, 'The coup leaders were clever but a regime that starts by shooting defenceless women is unlikely to have a peaceful future. Young Iraqis may believe that the revolution will usher in a free and just society, but I think they are destined to be disappointed.'

'It was by taking over Baghdad Radio in the early morning that the coup leaders were able to get a mob out into the streets,' Ralph replied.

'Life and death are in the power of the tongue. As true in 1958 as 1947,' Major Mac said.

Ralph thought of the anti-British broadcasts he and Major Mac had studied in Palestine, and how they had inspired hatred of the British Army.

'How did you find Jerusalem this time?' Major Mac asked.

'I only saw one half of it,' Ralph replied. 'The Palestinians and Israelis are inhabiting different parts of the same city and you cannot cross between the two.'

'What about the rest of the country?'

'There are raids across the border. The Palestinians start them and the Israelis respond disproportionately. This works for the Israelis in the short term but builds up more hatred, fuelling the cycle of violence. Who do you think has right on their side?' asked Ralph.

'Both peoples want the same piece of land and both have a right to it.'

'What chance is there of resolving the conflict?' asked Ralph.

'The two sides have to find a compromise, which is as diffi-cult to achieve today as it was in 1947. Without one the fighting will continue, with greater or lesser intensity, indefinitely.'

After supper Major Mac asked Ralph how his job was going and whether he was still hoping to get into the Foreign Service. Ralph said that he was planning to try for the late-entry compe-tition in a few months' time.

'Meanwhile,' he added, 'I am enjoying Beirut, although missing my friends in England.'

As if reading his mind Major Mac asked, 'One in particular?'

Ralph hesitated. He did not normally discuss his emotional life with anyone. Then, realizing that he would value Major Mac's advice, he nodded. 'A longstanding one from university. I am not sure what to do.'

'Do you love her?'

'I was not sure back in London. But since going abroad, I find I miss her a lot.'

'When you let an opportunity to love pass, you never know whether you will get another,' Major Mac said.

Ralph managed to get on a flight out of Baghdad a couple of days later. He had had a fascinating if alarming experience there. As the plane lifted off the runway, he could not help feeling a sense of relief. It would be good to get back to Beirut.

On arrival, the first thing he did was to call round at the embassy to collect his mail. He hoped there would be a letter from Mary whom he had not heard from for longer than usual. His spirits rose as he recognized her handwriting and put the envelope, along with others, in his pocket to read later in the quiet of his flat.

It was early evening by the time he got back there and, having made himself a cup of tea, he settled down in an armchair to enjoy his mail. An amusing letter from his mother gave some family news. He noted with pleasure that the new *Country Life* had arrived. A letter from his club informed him that his annual subscription had gone down to nine guineas a year since, being abroad, he qualified as a Supernumerary Member. A letter from an old school friend informed him that he had become a teacher. He had kept the envelope addressed to him in Mary's elegant, sloping handwriting to the last. He opened the envelope and read:

'Dear Ralph,

I have been worried about you since I gathered from your last letter that you were about to visit Baghdad. I hope that you were not caught up in the troubles there. I was shocked to read about the murder of the young king and royal princesses, also of the sacking of the British Embassy and killing of one of its members. The sacking must have been a terrifying experience for the embassy staff.

After referring to these harrowing events, it seems almost inappropriate to tell you of my own good news. I am engaged and will be getting married next month to Charles Graham, who you will remember from Cambridge. He asked me to send you his best wishes and we hope that you may be able to come to the wedding, though I expect this is unlikely unless you can arrange some official business in London to coincide with it!

As you can imagine I am frantically busy making arrangements for the wedding while continuing with my job.

Do make sure to let me know how you are.

With love from

Mary'

Ralph had known Charles at Cambridge but had not kept up with him. He was a nice man and he should have felt happy for Mary, but his only feeling was one of desolation. He realized that during the last few weeks he had raised his expectations to an unwarrantable degree. But what upset him most was the consciousness that he had not risked declaring himself. Looking back, he felt that at their last dinner together before his departure to Beirut, she was expecting him to say something, and the thought had indeed crossed his mind, but he had not acted on it and the end of the evening had consequently gone a bit flat. Now it was too late. Better to have tried and failed than not to have tried at all. Memories of affectionate moments came flooding back to haunt him, the most poignant being that of Mary's first visit to his digs in Cambridge and of her coming in out of the rain and sitting in front of the fire. He had taken her for granted and allowed the spark kindled on that occasion to die. With the end of their relationship went his hopes for the future. Was there still any point in continuing his work with the Overseas Development Administration or of trying to transfer to the Foreign Service? He had lost his purpose in life.

IV

WHITEHALL

Late have I loved you, beauty ever old yet ever new!
Late have I loved you!
You were within me, but I was outside.
There I sought you, as I rushed about among
the beautiful things you had made.
You were within me, but I was not with you.

St Augustine

Returning to Beirut after experiencing the Revolution in July
1958, Ralph was deeply distressed by the news of Mary's forth-
coming marriage. The assumptions he had begun to make
about his future had proved false and he was feeling bruised
and purposeless. In this state of mind exercise helped and while
out walking he found himself by the Catholic Church of St
Louis. He had been that way before and passed it by. But this
time something made him stop and go in. Perhaps it was the
memory of the devotion of the ethnically mixed congregation
at the Mass he had attended with Major Mac in Baghdad a
fortnight before.

Entering the church, he found it empty and sat down in a
pew at the back. He looked down the nave. A little red light flick-
ered near the altar. Some empty houses feel cold and unlived

in, their silence oppressive. However, here he found the silence soothing and the atmosphere warm. The pain in his head eased along with the conflicting thoughts which had been tormenting him. For the first time since reading Mary's letter he began to feel there might be a way forward. This experience began the process which led a year later to his becoming a Catholic.

The Catholic Church was helping him at this time of crisis. He hoped it would help him find a way ahead. He was instructed back in London by Father Henry, a Jesuit priest at Farm Street, to whom Major Mac had given him an introduction.

Father Henry guided him gently without any pressure and let him make up his own mind. Apart from his visit to the Church of St Louis, Ralph was influenced by the example of Major Mac and, further back, by the encouragement Father John had given them to pray while in the lifeboat. As a traveller he had been attracted to the universality of the Church. But above all it was the Mass and the Eucharist, and the emphasis on developing a relationship with the Lord, which attracted him.

Ralph returned from Beirut to London to try for the late-entry competition to the Diplomatic Service and rather to his surprise he succeeded. Thereafter he was posted to Jordan, Turkey, Nigeria, and Beirut again, with some spells in the Foreign Office in between. He was presently in charge of the Middle Eastern Section. Now over fifty, he could expect at least one more foreign posting, hopefully as a Head of Mission. It would probably be in the Middle East on account of his experience and proficiency in Arabic. He had been awarded an OBE, mainly for serving a long stint in Beirut in stressful times. To the outside world he was a modest success, but he did not see himself that way.

That afternoon he was again immersed in the affairs of Iraq, though this time from a distance. The interdepartmental committee meeting he had been attending in the Cabinet Office to consider the implications for Britain of the outbreak of war in

September 1980 between Iraq and Iran over control of the Shatt al-Arab waterway was just concluding. The dozen or so middle-aged men in grey suits sitting around the fine old mahogany table, most of whom he knew slightly, were collecting up their papers and pushing back their chairs. The conference room with its high ceiling, delicate mouldings and nineteenth-century portraits of the great and the good seemed to have an air of stability about it contrasting with the violent events under discussion.

The chairman—a tall former sailor with piercing blue eyes, courteous yet authoritative—had stressed that Britain was neutral but had an interest in the conflict being resolved as soon as possible since it posed a potential threat to British investments in the Gulf and the free passage of oil supplies. Britain, he said, was in close consultation with the Americans, particularly over blocking any Soviet exploitation of the situation, and would use its influence with the two adversaries, in the case of Iran through an interest section in the Swedish Embassy since diplomatic relations had been broken off some time before, to further its aims. He thanked them for coming and promised to keep them informed through further meetings as necessary.

Ralph gazed out of the window. St James's Park was suffused in light while a breeze just stirred the flags on neighbouring buildings. He was reminded of Major Mac's prophetic remark to him over a drink in his bungalow the day after the revolution in Iraq, that a regime that began with the shooting of defenceless women was unlikely to have a peaceful future. In the intervening twenty-two years, one of the two original military leaders had executed the other, and three further coups had taken place, the last in 1968 headed by the Baathist, Ahmed Hassan al-Bakr, with his cousin, Saddam Hussein, as his deputy. In 1979 Saddam had encouraged his cousin to retire 'on health grounds' and assumed the presidency himself. Almost his first act was to accuse fifty-five of his fellow Baath Party members of conspiracy and to execute twenty-two of them a few days later. The next year he declared war on Iran.

Ralph came out of his reverie to find that most of the other members of the committee had already left the room. He got up and followed them, nodding to a group who were standing talking by the door. As he passed, he heard one of them say softly, 'Poor old sod, he looks crumpled.' He knew it was a reference to himself. Pity is a killer. He was very tired, his workload having been exceptionally heavy what with keeping in touch with British Missions in the Middle East and providing briefings for ministers. He stepped out into Whitehall, walked towards Westminster and turned down King Charles Street. He needed to drop off the classified papers in his briefcase at the Foreign Office before going home. Having opened his cupboard and put them away, he scrambled the combination lock and then checked that all the window catches were closed and that there were no loose papers lying in trays. His dirty coffee cup caught his eye and he took it to the Gents next door to wash it. Thinking of the remark he had just overheard, he glanced up at the mirror above the basin. His face looked thin and grey like a nervous bird. His eyes were slightly bloodshot and dull. Returning to his office he picked up his coat and briefcase, switched the lights off and proceeded along the corridor and down the stairs. He said 'Goodnight' to the security guard on duty at the entrance to the building and, with relief at having finished with the Office for the day, descended Clive Steps and crossed Horse Guards Road into the park.

It was after 6 p.m. A light breeze massaged his temples. The calls of swans and coots and an odd seagull mingled with the sighing of the wind in the plane trees. Two mallards wheeled high above him, then, with their wings half folded and fixed like jet fighters, glided steeply down towards the water. Ralph lost them in the fading light. The days were already shortening.

Soon he would be facing another winter and the thought came to him, as it had several times lately, that his own life was ebbing. He was over the top and, although he was doing an interesting and useful job, he felt that something was missing.

During his talks with Father Henry at the time of his conversion he had accepted that his relationship with Mary was over. However, he still longed for affection and considered that marriage should remain his aim. Since then he had had several relationships which, through his fault, had fizzled out. He had begun to recognize a pattern in them and had become wary of involvement for fear of falsely arousing others' affections. At present he was not in any relationship.

Ralph knew deep down that he was working too hard to avoid facing up to himself and who he was, because he feared that to do so might require him to make changes to the direction of his life. Meanwhile his faith was helping him cope and he attended Mass on his way home if he got off in time. Recently that had been the best part of the day for him. As in that church in Beirut long ago, his worries seemed to recede there, and he felt at peace.

Occupied with these thoughts he found that he had reached Birdcage Walk. He crossed the road and walked along Buckingham Gate. As he turned down Palace Street he caught the strains of a once-familiar song he had often listened to on his record player in Palestine, the tune of which Mary had played for him in her room at Cambridge—'if I loved you, time and again I would try to say all I'd want you to know...' He looked round and saw that the song was coming from a parked car in which a young couple were sitting close together. He had not thought of Mary for a while, but the music brought her back to him. He never played his record of Carousel because he did not like to be reminded that he had let his 'golden chances' pass him by.

A few moments later he walked up the steps into Westminster Cathedral. There was a Mass in progress, although he knew he was late for it. He knelt at the back so as not to disturb those already there and listened to the priest reading the words of the Canon. That evening he found it hard to concentrate. He prayed for Mary and for his mother, who had recently died and whom he greatly missed.

Ralph waited behind for a minute or two after the Mass had ended while the other members of the congregation walked back down the aisle past him. Most of them were middle-aged or older and several were lame. One way or another, he thought, they were all in need of healing. Just as he was about to get up, he noticed an elderly lady with a striking profile. He was sure that he had seen her somewhere before. A few moments later, on his way out, he found her studying the Notice of Services near the exit. She looked up as he passed and for a second their eyes met. He recognized her instantly. Summoning up all his courage he said, 'Forgive me, but I think we have met before.' She looked at him blankly. 'You won't remember me, but I was one of the boys on the lifeboat in 1940 to whom you were so kind. My name is Ralph.'

Kathy, whom he realized must now be about eighty, gave him the same lovely smile that he recalled from all those years ago and said, 'Ralph, of course I remember you. How wonderful to see you.'

'Have you got time for a cup of coffee?' he asked. They made their way to a café close to the cathedral. After some polite enquiries about where each other lived and what they were doing, Ralph said, 'Although it's forty years ago, the sinking remains etched in my memory and I still dream about being abandoned by that cargo vessel.'

'My memories of those eight days, and even more nights, also remain all too vivid,' Kathy said, 'and I found the aftermath difficult to cope with. When I got on board the destroyer I had nothing with me, not even a handkerchief or a toothbrush let alone a nightdress. On landing, important locals wanted to talk to me, first in Gourock and then in Glasgow. I felt exhausted and was finding speaking painful.'

'I felt alright to begin with,' Ralph said. 'But a week later I was desperately tired yet unable to sleep. I had to go into hospital for two nights.' Ralph paused. 'I would have liked to see you again and talk about it all. People who hadn't shared our experience couldn't understand. I have kept in touch with Ronnie, the eldest boy in our group. We realized how much we owed to you and the lifeboat crew for our survival.' Ralph looked into her eyes.

'We were both so lucky to survive,' Kathy said, 'and I still mourn those young girls in my charge who didn't.'

Kathy had to get back to see someone at her flat, but before parting they exchanged addresses and agreed to meet again. There was a lot more Ralph would have liked to discuss with her.

As Ralph walked home, he thought about Kathy. Looking back, he realized that she was the first woman he had loved. Although their relationship had not lasted long, it had been intense due to the circumstances. He remembered the sadness of saying goodbye to her the day after their arrival in Gourock and how she had kissed him. From what she had said, he concluded that she was living alone. She had gone back to teaching the piano after the war. It was what she enjoyed doing and she was still giving private lessons in London. She must have used her talents well and been true to herself, Ralph reflected. He had not realized that Kathy was a Catholic but now he remembered that she and Father John had talked together a lot, sometimes in French so as not to alarm the children when discussing their perilous situation.

Ralph lived in an early twentieth-century mansion flat a
short distance from the cathedral. There were eight flats in
the building, which had an old-fashioned lift and a porter on
duty during the day. His flat on the fourth floor was quiet with
high ceilings and well-proportioned rooms, which suited the
paintings and furniture he had inherited from his mother. He
had also inherited her other assets and with his salary was now
comfortably off. He switched on the lights and poured himself a
whisky. Kathy's words, 'We were both so lucky to survive,' resonated with him. Having, unlike most of the children on the ship,
been given another chance, had he made good use of it?

Wishing to avoid a gloomy train of thought, he looked at
the bookcase beside him. His eye lit on T.S. Eliot's *The Cocktail
Party*. Opening the book at random he found Miss Celia
Coplestone who, after the painful ending of a relationship and
torn between human and divine love, asks Sir Henry Harcourt-
Reilly, a psychiatrist, 'which way is better?' Reilly replies,

> 'Neither way is better.
> Both ways are necessary. It is also necessary
> To make a choice between them.'

Ralph knew that he had put off making important choices in
his life. It was the way to end up in what Reilly called, 'the final
desolation of solitude in the phantasmal world of imagination,
shuffling memories and desires.' Celia had claimed that that was
the hell she had been in and Reilly had replied, 'It isn't hell till
you become incapable of anything else.'

That night Ralph dreamt about Mary. He was in a fast-flowing river and she was on the bank, looking at him fearfully. He
desperately wanted to reach her, but the current was too strong
and, as he was swept downstream, he could see her in the distance still looking towards him.

Ralph woke up feeling unhappy and insecure. His chance

meeting with Kathy, though delightful in itself, had made him question whether he was being true to himself. And, as he walked to work, the vividness of his dream about Mary remained with him, opening up the old wound made by the sudden rupture of their relationship. He thought of her beauty, of the life they could have shared and of the children they might have had. The painful feelings he had experienced the day he received Mary's letter in Beirut, informing him that she was getting married, came back to him.

On that earlier occasion his visit to the Catholic Church had helped him. And he had recently heard that Father Henry, the priest who had received him into the Church, had returned to Farm Street after working in South America for several years. Acting intuitively, Ralph telephoned him and asked if he could come and see him. Father Henry said he remembered their past conversations well and would much look forward to meeting him again.

V

BUS RIDE

'Men never do evil so completely
and cheerfully as when they do it from
religious conviction.'

Blaise Pascal (1623-1662)

Father Henry greeted him warmly when he arrived at Farm Street. Unsurprisingly, given the passage of twenty-two years, many of which had been spent in a hot and humid climate, he looked considerably older.

'I'm sorry to trouble you so soon after your return from Guyana with something I ought to be able to sort out for myself,' Ralph said as soon as they were settled in comfortable chairs in Father Henry's study.

Father Henry smiled. 'I've been back here for six months and it now feels as if I'd never been away. It's a pleasure to see you again, and it sometimes helps to discuss a problem with another person even if you do eventually have to solve it yourself.'

'Well,' Ralph said, 'I have an interesting and well-paid job, for which many people would envy me, but I have increasingly felt something was missing from my life. As I told you when I first came to see you, I was in love with a girl who married someone else. Her image has stayed with me and made it hard for me to sustain relationships with other women. Two days ago I had an unsettling dream.' Ralph told Father Henry about it.

'I'm no expert on dream analysis,' Father Henry said, 'but your dream could be expressing your regret for lost love and fear of ending up alone.'

Ralph nodded, remembering his reading of *The Cocktail Party* that evening.

'When we talked before,' Father Henry continued, 'I think you said that your relationship with Mary had ended, but it sounds as if her image has stayed with you and that you used it, either consciously or unconsciously, to avoid committing yourself to anyone else. You told me that it was lack of courage that stopped you committing yourself to Mary when you had the chance. Have you considered that another reason may have been that deep down you were undecided as to what you really wanted to do? It is hard to commit yourself to living with another person if you are not sure what sort of life you want to lead.'

'Looking back over the years since I last saw you,' Ralph said, 'every emotional move I have made seems to have ended in a cul-de-sac.'

'Perhaps you have been searching for happiness in the wrong place—from other things, beautiful things, part of God's creation but outside yourself—whereas God may want you to turn inwards and listen to what your own heart is telling you.'

Ralph felt they were treading on dangerous ground but forced himself to go on. 'I may have avoided listening to my heart because I feared where it might lead me. I recognize that I have put off making choices about my life and that I may have hurt other people as a result. Since my mother's recent death there is no one who depends on me. I attend Mass after work whenever I can and find that is the best part of the day. I now feel I would like to do something that's more directly of service to other people.'

'I was sorry to learn of your mother's death,' Father Henry said. 'I can understand how you feel, but before you can help other people you need to be at peace with yourself. Perhaps you are searching for something you have not yet found. Are you wondering whether you might have a vocation?'

'Yes,' Ralph said.

Father Henry suggested he set himself a time limit of a few months to come to a decision. In the meantime, he could think more deeply about the idea, undertake some reading and go on a retreat. They talked on for a few minutes. Ralph enquired about the state of the Church in Guyana and Father Henry asked him about his own postings abroad for the Foreign Office since they had last met.

It was two days before Ralph could get an appointment to see Bob Murray, the Head of Personnel, whom he knew and liked. He was younger than Ralph but had been in the Foreign Office longer, having joined straight from university. Unlike Ralph he was a high-flyer, having served in Washington and been private secretary to ministers. Ralph explained his position and asked if he could be allowed to remain in his present post in London for the next six months while he made up his mind. In agreeing to this request Bob pointed out that the Foreign Office had few members who could equal Ralph's command of Arabic and even fewer who possessed as much experience of being at the sharp end in the Middle East. He also recognized that Ralph's present job was a demanding one and he had hoped that he would have been able to offer Ralph a final foreign posting which would have been to his liking. In conclusion he said that Ralph's resignation would be deeply regretted. Ralph replied that he much appreciated what Bob had said and that he would carefully consider matters before coming to a decision.

Emerging from Bob's office Ralph felt that he also needed some unofficial advice and he at once thought of Major Mac, who was now retired. Major Mac spent the summers in Scotland while wintering in London to see more of his children and to keep his mind active by reviewing old files at the Ministry of Defence. They met regularly for a drink after work. Ralph found him wise and totally discreet. He knew that Major Mac was in London at the moment and they arranged to meet for a drink after work at the club to which they both belonged.

As he walked up St James's Street Ralph remembered that many years before in Baghdad he had taken Major Mac into his confidence over his relationship with Mary. Pushing through the swing doors of the club, he said good evening to the hall porter.

'Good evening, Mr Sebright. The brigadier is in the library.'

Ralph walked upstairs in some trepidation. Major Mac, who was standing by the table in the centre of the room flipping over the pages of magazines, turned round as Ralph came in. He had gone a bit grey but still looked very distinguished. Moments later they were settled in deep leather armchairs with glasses of whisky.

After Ralph had enquired after Major Mac's family, he said, 'I wanted to ask your advice about something. I am considering leaving the Foreign Service and becoming a priest.'

To Ralph's relief, Major Mac took the news calmly, saying, 'Ultimately it has to be a personal decision. But let me act as devil's advocate. With your knowledge of Arabic and the Middle East you are doing valuable work for the country. The Foreign Service is short of staff with your skills. And the Church must greatly appreciate having a Catholic in such an influential position.'

Ralph countered, 'For some time I have not been required to use my Arabic or my rapport with Middle Easterners but have instead been wholly occupied with paper and committee work, which could be done equally well or better by others.'

'Alright,' Major Mac replied, 'but I still think you have a key role in the Foreign Service which you are only able to fulfil because of your years of experience. If you train to become a priest you are unlikely to be ordained much before you are sixty.'

Ralph said that he accepted the force of Major Mac's case and he would think about it further, but in the end it had to be a matter of conscience. They went on to talk about the old days in Palestine and Iraq and the present situation there.

It was not with the object of getting advice that Ralph next received some more. After meeting Kathy after Mass at Westminster Cathedral they had agreed to get in touch again for a longer talk about their shared experiences. In fulfilment of this agreement she had invited him round for coffee, as it happened, two days after his talk with Major Mac.

Her flat was in an old-fashioned mansion block, of which there were many in Victoria, rather like his own. It was plainly but comfortably furnished with some attractive watercolours on the walls and a piano in one corner of the sitting room.

As sometimes happens with people one sees at rare intervals, they talked freely about their lives. She asked him what he did and whether he was married. He told her about his situation and then asked her about her own. She said that she had always loved music and had wanted to give priority to using the talent she had been given, to play the piano. In her twenties and thirties she had both taught and performed. Just after the outbreak of the war she had got engaged to a soldier who also loved music, but he had been killed in action early on. She had taken the job of escorting evacuees as her contribution to the war effort. As he was aware, this role had turned out traumatic.

After the war she nearly married another man who was well off. Something had happened to put her off. One weekend she had to turn down an invitation from him because she was committed to giving a recital at a school. Unthinkingly, he had commented that she would not have to do this any more once they were married. She did get paid a little for giving such recitals, but money was not her main motive for taking them on. At that instant she had realized that he would never understand what made her want to perform, and that if she married him there would be a constant clash between what he expected of her and her deep commitment to her music.

Kathy believed that any artistic talent needed cherishing and often required its possessor to make sacrifices—emotional, financial, or both—in order to pursue it. She had given up performing some years back but had continued teaching and playing for her own enjoyment and that of her friends. In retrospect she had not regretted her decision to break off her engagement. Looking at Ralph she said, 'Perhaps the decision you are faced with now resembles, in some respects, the one I was faced with then.' Her words resonated with him.

Whereas *The Cocktail Party* and his dream had first caused him to consider making a change of direction in his life, it was the retreat over a long weekend that finally decided him to do so. At the end of a day that included a Mass and several discourses, feeling rather tired, he visited the chapel on his own where he had a sense of the presence of God, along with a feeling of peace and joy, such as he had never experienced before. Time seemed to stand still and he was conscious of nothing except the wonder of the present moment.

In spite of Ralph's age, the Archdiocese of Westminster accepted his candidature and decided that he should go for his training to the Beda College in Rome, which ran a four-year course intended for older men and where, away from London, it might be easier for him to make a clean break from his old life.

The Beda Pontifical College was founded in 1852, mainly for Anglican clergymen who wished to convert to Rome. He found it peaceful despite having to study hard. He realized that for a long time he had been too pressured to listen to his own heart. Moreover, having time for prayer and to be still made him more receptive to others and he discovered kindred spirits among his fellow seminarians whose company he was able to enjoy. And Rome was a pleasant place to live, with its friendly people, beautiful buildings, lovely light and colours. Four years passed quickly by.

As Major Mac had forecast, Ralph was almost sixty by the time of his ordination, after which he was appointed curate to an elderly priest in a West London parish. When a few years later the priest retired on health grounds, Ralph took over the parish. He found the role of parish priest fulfilling. In consecrating the bread and wine during Mass and offering himself up to God with Christ's body and blood he felt that he was doing what he had been created for. He never again experienced the same intense consciousness of the presence of God as he had done in the chapel on the retreat, but the memory of it having been better than anything else in his life remained vivid and sustained his resolve when troubled by doubts or depression. He was content with the decision he had made over his life, and his work of ministering to his parishioners gave him joy. This more than made up for the occasional worries and frustrations which went with being a parish priest.

On account of his good health, willingness to continue and the shortage of priests, he was allowed to remain in his parish longer than usual and past the age of seventy-five. In addition to his parish duties he had, for some years, been given responsibility by the archdiocese to act as chaplain to a prison, holding a weekly service there and being available to Catholic prisoners who wanted to see a priest. This role involved liaison with an Anglican priest and an Imam who also held services at the prison. They were people of the Book and got on well. Ralph especially liked the Imam, who was of Palestinian origin.

Their experience of the prison had bonded them—being searched, having to listen sympathetically and trying to encourage depressed people—as had his knowledge of Arabic and the Middle East. They both appreciated that it was a privilege to enter the prison but were always glad to get out.

Ralph took the opportunity to improve his knowledge of the Quran and of how—through arousing rage by portraying Islam as under attack from the West and making an idealistic appeal to self-sacrifice for God's sake—young Muslims were persuaded by Islamists to become suicide bombers. The Iman referred him to Shariah Law, which forbids violence against civilians, and gave him some Quranic verses which made clear that the killing of innocent people could have no place in Islam. The Arabic words were beautiful, and Ralph had found himself repeating them out loud.

On a sunny afternoon in August 2006 he went to visit a sick friend in Albion Street, just north of Hyde Park. Because he had taken her Communion, he was wearing a dog collar. After leaving her he walked down to the Bayswater Road, intending to take a bus from Marble Arch to Victoria. He found himself passing the Convent at Tyburn, where the Blessed Sacrament is exposed continuously, and decided to spend a few minutes there. Inside the chapel was a list of those who were martyred at Tyburn. He knew the place of old, and when visiting it was always conscious of the huge risks Catholic priests had run in exercising their pastoral duties in the sixteenth and seventeenth centuries—over a hundred Catholics had been executed at Tyburn between 1535 and 1681—in marked contrast to his own comfortable lifestyle in the twenty-first century.

Emerging from the Convent, he crossed Bayswater Road and the North Carriage Drive and entered the park. Walking eastwards under ancient plane trees, he crossed over Park Lane and made his way to the Marble Arch bus stop. Traffic was beginning to build up and the first Victoria-bound bus, a Number 390, was full. However, he got on to the next, a Number 13, and took a seat downstairs about halfway up the bus.

As the bus gathered speed, he noticed that the young man in front of him was talking on his mobile. Ralph's antennae, sensitised over the years in Beirut, sent out alarm signals. It was barely a year after 7/7 and the man was speaking in Arabic. He seemed to be telling his respondent where he was in relation to Victoria Station. There was nothing remarkable about the content of the conversation except that the man sounded extremely agitated. Ralph looked over the back of the seat and saw that he had a knapsack on his lap. Why had he not placed it in the luggage rack or on the floor? Having stopped talking he was now looking at a sheet of Arabic text. It was too far away for Ralph to read, but instinct told him that it was a prayer sheet and that the man was a Jihadist. If so, any defensive action Ralph took, like pulling the communication cord, could cause the man to panic and explode his device. What should he do? Acting intuitively, Ralph began to recite in Arabic one of the verses the Imam at the prison had given him, making clear that the killing of innocent people was forbidden by Islam. He leant forward and spoke loud enough for the man in front to hear him, but not so loud as to attract the attention of other passengers. The message was apposite: 'Remember that you are always under the looks of God and on the verge of death ... Do not shed women, children and old people's blood'. As he finished, he heard the man gasp but he did not turn round. There was still some way to go to the next stop.

Ralph had witnessed the way violence breeds violence, first as a soldier in Palestine and later as a diplomat posted to trouble spots. Now he hoped that for once, as a priest, he might be able to break the chain. The seconds ticked by slowly. Then, as the bus slowed down, the man rose from his seat holding the knapsack. Ralph did not look up so as to avoid eye contact. They were only two stops away from Victoria. He felt immense relief as the man got off and the bus moved away.

Ralph's relief was such that, as the bus slowed for the next stop, he hardly noticed that a grey-haired middle-aged woman in a mackintosh had stopped by his seat and was glaring down at him. 'You lot cause evil in the world,' she said. He felt her saliva hit his cheek. Taken aback he stared up at her. She did not wait for his response but continued down the gangway and off the bus.

Having travelled peacefully around London by bus for years, to suddenly be dealt a double-whammy left him emotionally drained. The last time he had been spat on was during the sacking of the British Embassy in Baghdad in 1958.

Back in the presbytery, he made himself a strong cup of coffee and wrote a letter to the Metropolitan Police about the first incident, saying that given 7/7 last year he felt he ought to report an event that he had witnessed. He then explained that due to the circumstances he could not give a detailed description of the young man on the bus.

He then wondered what to do about the second incident. The woman had probably had a personal or family experience in which a priest had betrayed her trust. It could have been over child abuse, past cases of which had recently been surfacing in the press and undermining the Church's moral authority. There was little he could do, apart from informing the other members of the Deanery at their next monthly meeting. He decided to do nothing. He had no idea what had caused the woman to act in this way. Hence, he could not judge her. Jesus had been spat on at Calvary. He remembered the relevant scripture: 'I offered my back to those who struck me, I did not cover my face against spittle.' If the wholly innocent Christ had accepted it, he himself, whose life had been full of false turns, should do likewise.

Ralph got the opportunity to discuss the first incident with the Iman, whose judgement he respected, on his next visit to the prison. On hearing that Ralph had recited the Quranic verse to the young man, the Imam commented, 'If he was a Jihadi, you were lucky it worked. One of our difficulties is that few of the Jihadis have much knowledge of Islam, so an appeal to Islamic teaching is not necessarily effective. Your young man may have reacted the way he did out of sheer shock at hearing these Arabic words, forbidding the action he was about to take, coming from the seat behind him at the very moment he was asking God to strengthen his resolve.'

Ralph also received a polite letter of thanks from the Metropolitan Police.

VI

ARMAGEDDON

'And I have asked to be
Where no storms come,
Where the green swell is in the havens dumb
And out of the swing of the sea.'

Gerard Manley Hopkins
1844-1889

Ralph was again in a bus, he realized, as a jolt woke him up and he looked out of the window. They were driving in the shadow of a high wall covered in graffiti. A painted dove held an olive branch in its beak with a sniper's rifle pointing at its heart. A notice read, 'TO EXIST IS TO RESIST'. He knew the wall had been built to protect Israelis from terrorist attack, but running in and out and round Jewish settlements it caused the Palestinians much hardship, sometimes cutting them off from their place of work, while also dividing families and communities.

Further on he saw a gleaming white Israeli settlement astride a hill to the east of the road to Bethlehem, where he and his fellow pilgrims were going for the day. When the bus stopped mid-morning at a checkpoint, a hooded man stood surrounded by Israeli soldiers, and he wondered what his Palestinian farmer hosts at lunch on the banks of the Jordan River in 1958, who had held Britain responsible for the loss of their best land, would have said to him today if any of them were still alive. Although fifty-nine years had passed since then, he still felt personally involved in the conflict between Palestinians and Israelis.

Ralph was getting increasingly frail and he found himself dropping off quite often. When he had mentioned this to his doctor, whom he had seen before committing himself to the pilgrimage, he had been told that everything was slowing down with age but that, in his doctor's opinion, it would not be irresponsible for him to go if he wanted to.

Ralph had retired at eighty but his successor, with the agreement of the archdiocese, had allowed him to retain a bedsit in the presbytery. There, without any administrative responsibilities, he was still able to stand in for local priests who were sick or on holiday.

Many things drew Ralph back to Palestine, not least his military service there. The bus was now approaching Bethlehem, whence Christ's family had fled to Egypt to avoid persecution. The role of refugees had always been a hard one, whether two thousand years ago or today. And Ralph was still haunted by unhappy memories of Jewish refugees arriving in Haifa in 1947 and being forcibly unloaded by the army and deported to camps in Cyprus. He wondered what had happened to the beautiful girl who had glared at him that afternoon in the docks.

Arriving in Bethlehem, they attended Mass in the Church of the Nativity before having lunch at the Arab Society for Rehabilitation. Ralph learnt that the society, founded in 1960 as one of Leonard Cheshire's homes, was a leading provider of medical, surgical and rehabilitation services, empowering disabled people to pursue full and meaningful lives, in Bethlehem and across the West Bank. Their bus returned them to Jerusalem in time for dinner.

The next day was also likely to arouse disturbing memories

for Ralph as his group was to spend two nights in Tiberias, calling in at Acre on the way there. Ralph had not been back to Acre since being stationed in the Haifa region in 1947. Acre was close to Nahariya where he had been wounded.

He thought of Major Mac and Ronnie who had both come to visit him in hospital in Haifa. He had seen the former regularly until his death a few years back. Ronnie, as far as he knew, was still alive. His intelligence and determination had earned him a commission. He left the army as a major, married and joined a security firm. This must have proved profitable because he had made a generous donation to a charitable fund which helped the poor in Ralph's parish, some of them refugees from the Middle East. Ralph remembered Ronnie's characteristic remark when they first met again after his ordination. 'Well, Father, you certainly took your time.'

The evening before their departure, after prayers in their hotel, Monsignor Bob, who knew of Ralph's experiences in Palestine during his military service, had asked him to say a few words about the situation then. He had done so, concentrating mainly on the pressure on Britain to allow large numbers of Jewish immigrants to settle in Palestine after the war and the fierce opposition this met from the Palestinians, leaving the British Army and administration uncomfortably in the middle, trying to keep the peace and getting shot at by both sides, but mainly by the formidable Jewish Underground. He mentioned briefly that he himself had been wounded by Underground fighters escaping from the prison at Acre and had subsequently been given first aid by an elderly Jewish lady at Nahariya.

The next day was fine and by mid-morning they had reached Megiddo, also known as Armageddon, where according to the Book of Revelation, the final battle between the forces of good and evil would take place. Ralph remembered that it guarded the pass through the Carmel mountain range controlling the route from Damascus to Egypt, and had witnessed battles throughout the ages, one of the most recent being the defeat of the Ottomans by General Allenby in 1917, just a hundred years ago. It seemed an innocent-looking stretch of land made up of fields of vegetables broken up by some olive groves.

As they approached Acre the countryside began to look familiar to Ralph. The midday light was strong, and he could tell that the sea was not far distant. The driver parked the bus in the shade of some majestic palm trees standing up against a high stone wall outside the old fortress. They were told to take a lunch break at a restaurant of their choice, and to be back in the bus an hour and a half later for a talk before proceeding on their way to Tiberias.

Ralph and Monsignor Bob headed for the harbour where several restaurants offered fresh fish. They chose one close to the sea and ordered prawns with a salad and a glass of white wine. A light breeze kept them cool enough in the sun. Ralph already knew the Monsignor slightly. He was a cradle Catholic from a Warwickshire family which gave them a bond, Ralph's own family having originated from Warwickshire. Although much younger than Ralph, he had served in a number of parishes around the Archdiocese of Birmingham. Ralph found him wise and kind with a nice sense of humour. In the current ecumenical climate he had proved good at getting on with the representatives of other Churches. He had a deep knowledge of the historical background to the New Testament. And, apart from God, he was passionate about cricket.

As they settled down to enjoy their lunch Ralph said, 'It's curious to come back here again. Although seventy years have passed, things look much the same.'

'What was your life like then?' Bob asked.

Ralph thought of his forced unloading of exhausted illegal Jewish immigrants from ships, of his unsuccessful search for the two kidnapped British sergeants, of the anger in the officers' mess over their killing, and of Major Mac. 'Quite challenging for a first job, but I made one lasting friend there—my company commander. He was a Catholic and was influential in both my conversion and ordination. I also remember his comment on the situation then facing us, an unusual one for a regular soldier: "Violence breeds violence". His words have resonated with me ever since.'

'Talking of violence, did you have any qualms when we passed through Armageddon this morning?' Bob asked.

Ralph thought of R.H. Benson's 1907 novel, *Lord of the World*, about a conflict between two charismatic leaders, one centred on God and the other on man. The conflict turned violent with an air attack on the Pope and those remaining loyal to him in the Holy Land, only thwarted at the last moment by the rising of a fierce dust storm. And he remembered Nevil Shute's scenario in his novel, *On the Beach*, where a year after a nuclear Third World War, the inhabitants of Melbourne awaited death as radioactive clouds drifted slowly southward, eliminating all life in their path.

'Some,' Ralph said. 'The world is in a worrying state at present—though it often has been before. The only difference now is that mortals have ample means to destroy it.'

'According to the Gospels, only the Father knows when the world is to end,' Bob said.

'Jesus also warned that great suffering and persecution of his followers would precede the end of the world and that the Church would pass through a final trial, which would shake the faith of believers,' Ralph added. 'Arguably, with the persecution and martyrdom of more Christians in the twentieth and early twenty-first centuries than ever before, and with the impact of the current child abuse scandal, both these conditions are met.' The abuse scandal, he thought, had mushroomed hugely since he had been spat on in the bus some years back. 'So, as to your query about qualms, the safest answer is "Don't know" but "Stand ready, because the Son of Man is coming at an hour you do not expect".'

'I think we had better finish off the wine!' Bob said.

They walked across a paved square bounded on one side by the ancient sea walls on top of which were children playing, closely watched by nervous parents. Back at the bus, they were joined by an Israeli couple, one of whom Ralph assumed would be giving them the promised talk. But as their tour guide explained, the couple were married and both doctors, and would each be giving a separate short talk.

The man spoke first about the history of Acre. He was an academic, a professor of ancient history. Acre, he said, was an exceptionally old city in existence under Alexander the Great, the Egyptians, the Romans, the Crusaders and the Ottomans. He digressed briefly about each period. Then, turning to the buildings, he said that the Ottomans had replaced the twelfth-century sea walls and built a fortress on the thirteenth-century foundations of the Crusader castle. Today the fortress was the Museum of Underground Prisoners and, he added, he would leave it to his wife to explain how this had come about.

His wife took over the microphone and started by saying that, unlike her husband, she was a doctor of medicine. She then recounted that the British during the Mandate had used the fortress as a prison and that, during Israel's struggle for independence after the Second World War, both Jews and Arabs had been held there. Among the Jews were many members of the Jewish Underground. This was why it was now designated a museum in their memory. Some Jews had been executed there and some others had escaped. Her own family had been indirectly involved in one such escape.

In 1947, she continued, some members of the Underground

had broken out of the prison with outside help from their organisation. Then, armed and fleeing in what looked like a British military vehicle, they had passed close to some British soldiers who had tried to wave them down. Fearing recapture, the Jews had fired on the soldiers and wounded a young British officer close to Nahariya, who had become separated from the rest of his men. The officer made his way with difficulty to the nearest habitation which happened to belong to her grandparents. In spite of the hostile attitude of Jews to the British Army at that time, her grandmother had taken him in and, having some nursing experience, she had treated him, stemming the flow of blood. Her grandmother did not know what happened to the officer, who was taken to hospital, but she subsequently received a letter of thanks from his commanding officer.

Ralph listened to the doctor's words in amazement. At the end of her talk his fellow pilgrims gave her a round of applause. To their credit, none of them even looked in his direction. Ralph realized that, if any move was to be made, it was up to him to make it. Hesitating for a moment, he got up and proceeded to the front of the bus where the doctor and her husband were sitting. Monsignor Bob, who was sitting across the gangway from them, guessing what was in Ralph's mind, got up so that Ralph could take over his seat.

Ralph leant across the gangway and, stretching out his hand, said to the doctor of medicine, 'I am the person to whom your grandmother gave first aid in 1947. According to the hospital where I was afterwards treated, she could well have saved my life.'

The doctor looked at him in astonishment. 'How extraordinary to meet you after so many years a few miles from Nahariyah.'

'It's the first time I've been back here,' Ralph said.

'My grandmother saved a good life,' the doctor replied, glancing at his dog collar.

'I'm not sure about that,' Ralph said smiling. 'But I'm very grateful to her for doing so. It was a time when the British Army was hated by many in Palestine and I can hear her, as if it were yesterday, telling your grandfather that under the Torah they could not turn a wounded man away from their door. Perhaps she was also influenced by the words of the Talmud, "Save one life, save the world".'

Ralph and the doctor talked on for a minute or two before exchanging addresses and bidding each other a fond farewell.

During the bus drive to Galilee, Ralph thought about the lady who had treated him long ago. He wished there had been time to learn more about her, especially her early life. However, having read about the emigrants to Israel from Central Europe before the Second World War, he could imagine it. With her fine bone structure, she must have been beautiful as a young woman. And judging from the photographs of her antecedents in her sitting room, she would have come from a cultured background. Wealthy and civilised, with servants to look after her, her position in a pro-vincial German town around 1930 would have seemed assured. A good education would have been followed by an enjoyable social life, with dances and tennis parties. Then suddenly all this would be at risk. She might have noticed a certain coldness developing towards her on the part of her Christian friends. Then her parents could have decided that, in the long-term interests of her safety, she should join some cousins in Palestine. There she would have experienced a greatly reduced standard of living. A few years later, after the outbreak of war, the flow of letters from the members of her family who had remained in Germany would have ceased. She would then have had to wait until the end of the war to have her worst fears confirmed.

This train of thought reminded him of the affidavit he had read in Yad Vashem a few days before of Hermann Friedrich Groebe, a German engineer who had risked his life to save Jews in his employment and had been recognized as being Righteous Among the Nations. Hermann had witnessed mass executions at Dubno on 5 October 1942 and he remembered 'a girl, slim and with black hair, who as she passed close to me pointed to herself and said, "Twenty-three ..." The people, completely naked, went down some steps which were cut in the clay wall of the pit and clambered over the heads of the people lying there, to the place where the SS man directed them. They then lay down in front of the dead or injured people; some caressed those who were still alive and spoke to them in a low voice. Then I heard a series of shots.'

Of all Ralph had read about the Holocaust, the matter-of-fact courage of this girl, who should have had her life stretching ahead of her, had moved him most.

Having spent the night in Tiberias after his uncanny encounter with the Israeli doctor, Ralph found himself aboard ship again next morning. The sky was overcast as they set off to cross the Sea of Galilee in a wooden fishing boat said to resemble the one used by the Apostles. It was bigger than the lifeboat that had saved him from the giant Atlantic waves in 1940. This time, however, only a slight swell gently lifted the boat up and down. The crew cast out nets, partly for real and partly to remind their passengers of the Gospels, but no fish were caught that day.

From the far shore his group travelled by bus north-eastwards towards the border with Syria and Lebanon. The Galilean hills were covered in stones, their harsh grey relieved only by a few green irrigated patches and some olive groves on the lower-lying ground. They climbed upwards to the viewing point on the Golan Heights, from which it was said on a clear day Damascus was just visible. It was hazy at the summit, unfortunately, but good to be able to walk about and look through the scrub oak, acacia and thorn in the foreground towards the distant road on which the conversion of St Paul took place.

By the roadside around the summit yellow signs gave warning of the danger of mines, a reminder that Israel had enemies— Syria, who wanted the return of the Golan Heights occupied by Israel in 1967 after the Six Day War, and Iran, Syria's more powerful neighbour and supporter, who refused to acknowledge Israel's right to exist.

On the way back to Jerusalem the bus stopped at Nazareth, where Ralph was taken to the tiny Chapel of the Little Brothers of Jesus Caritas, dedicated to the Blessed Charles de Foucauld. It comprised a cream-coloured courtyard with plants climbing up the walls and a well in the centre. A charming girl showed them round. Inside the chapel on the left was a photograph of Father Charles, bearded and wearing a white habit, but it was his calm eyes that held Ralph's attention. From fast-living French cavalry officer in his youth, he had become in turn an explorer in Morocco, a Trappist monk and a gardener to the Convent of the Poor Clares in Nazareth, before becoming a priest and ultimately serving the Tuareg in Tamanrasset. He came to no harm on his many travels across the desert, usually on foot. It was men—anti-French Senussi tribesmen—who eventually killed him. Ralph had once visited Tamanrasset travelling home by car across the Sahara at the end of his posting to Nigeria in the sixties. Then it was soft sand that posed the main threat. Today it was Jihadis like the young man in the Number 13 bus, who increasingly posed a threat to desert travellers and to Christians living in the Sahel.

The next day, back in Jerusalem, Ralph visited the Hall of Names situated close to the Holocaust Museum. It had as its object the recording of the names of all those Jews who had perished, thereby underlining the sanctity of each human life and the tragedy of its loss. Since parting from the doctor in Acre, he had thought a lot about the words of the Talmud, 'Save one life, save the world', and the sometimes huge repercussions of the loss of one life, as in the case of the assassination by a Jewish student in 1995 of Yitzak Rabin, then Prime Minister of Israel as he left a peace rally in Tel Aviv.

The Israeli doctor had exclaimed at the coincidence of her meeting Ralph, whose life might have been saved by her grandmother. Ralph was not sure that he believed in coincidences. Over the years he had met up with people he had known before, seemingly by chance, but often some advantage, if only the revival of a friendship, had come out of it. The occasions when he had seen someone in these circumstances but had been too busy or feared reinvolvement and had avoided contact, hung heavily on his conscience. He accepted the truth of Gerald Vann's words in *The Divine Pity*: 'Every human relationship is an eternal responsibility'. He thought of the Number 13 bus in Park Lane. Was it a coincidence that he, an Arabic speaker, had come to sit in a bus behind a young Arab intent on setting off a bomb? He doubted it. Similarly, did his rereading of *The Cocktail Party* and his dream about being swept away from Mary by the current, which had led to a change in the direction of his life, occur by chance?

Thinking of Mary, he had first been struck by her photograph in a magazine in Palestine in 1947. Later, when they were seeing each other in London, he had told her about receiving first aid from the elderly lady. After her marriage, Mary and he had kept in touch by Christmas cards. They had not sought to see each other again. However, she had written to him from abroad to congratulate him on his ordination and to express her admiration for the courageous change he had made in mid-career. She hoped that he would derive peace and satisfaction from it. In the circumstances he thought he should send her a postcard, telling her of his meeting with the doctor. She was only two years younger than him, but he knew her address and that she was alive last Christmas. He described their pilgrimage in a few sentences and then wondered how to end up. After thinking for a moment, he wrote, 'I am so grateful for the happiness that we once shared. Love, Ralph'.

He wondered what his life would have been like had they married. It was profitless to speculate. And yet uninvited, T.S. Eliot's words from *Burnt Norton* came back to him:

> 'Footfalls echo in the memory
> Down the passage which we did not take
> Towards the door we never opened
> Into the rose garden.'

He might have shared his life with someone he loved. However, at the time cowardice and indecision had deterred him from going down that passage. Having repressed his emotions as a child, he had distrusted them as an adult. 'La coeur a ses raisons, que la raison ne connait point' (The heart has it reasons which reason knows nothing of). He wished that he had read Pascal earlier.

Actually though, marriage and priesthood had much in common—a commitment to please another person. And his eventual choice had taken courage too. As Pascal had also written, 'C'est le premier pas qui coute' (It is the first step which costs). Once taken, everything falls into place, and his priesthood had indeed brought him peace and satisfaction, along with love of a different but closely related kind, for all love comes from God. He had been privileged to share God with people, especially the elderly, the sick, the dying and those in prison. They had trusted him, and he had been able to continue serving them long after most of his contemporaries had retired. He hoped that Mary's marriage had brought her happiness too.

It was their second last day and, for old times' sake, Ralph invited Monsignor Bob to have a drink at the American Colony Hotel after they had had their early self-serve supper in their own hotel. It was only a few minutes' walk away. Ralph had booked a table in the vine-covered courtyard. Built circa 1870 for a Turkish merchant, it was converted into a hotel in the early twentieth century and ever since had been a haven for diplomats and journalists. Once seated, Ralph ordered some white wine which arrived with hummus and olives. The combination of wine and once familiar atmosphere was stimulating. When last there he was thirty, fit, with many options open, looking to new horizons. Now it was different. His back ached and he had difficulty putting on his socks. Nevertheless, he was happy with where he was.

Bob looked across at him. 'It must be strange coming back to one of your old haunts. Did you ever miss your diplomat's life after you resigned to become a priest?'

'At the time of my resignation I was finding my job demanding and unsatisfying. It was absorbing most of my energy leaving little over for other things. My emotional life had reached an impasse and I had allowed my other interests to lapse. I felt I was drying up inside. So I didn't miss my old job—it had become a grind of committee and paperwork within Whitehall.'

'What about the discipline of the Church ... obeying the bishop?'

'My introduction via the Beda was gentle and I could have left at any time if I had chosen to do so. Actually, I was relieved to be released from the pressure I had been under in the Foreign Office and to have time to think and pray.' Ralph paused. Looking back, the best bits of his Foreign Service career had been working in embassies abroad where he had found trying to get to the truth of what was happening fascinating. He had enjoyed the camaraderie of working with usually stimulating colleagues, also making friends with foreigners and learning about their culture. 'I enjoyed a lot of my earlier time in the Foreign Service, especially abroad. In tense times you get to know and depend on other members of the staff, and they on you. I found that experience helped me after becoming a priest.'

'I too found my time as a layman valuable,' Bob said, 'although it was comparatively short. I first considered becoming a priest at school but thought I would gain some experience of the world before making up my mind. So I went to Warwick University to read history for three years. I enjoyed my time there but decided to stick to my original intention. Looking back my university years were important to me. As a priest, people come to you for advice and it's easier to offer a layman good advice if you've been one yourself.'

Ralph nodded. They talked on for a while. Eventually Ralph, beginning to tire, said, 'While we are alone here, I would like to say how rewarding and enjoyable it's been for me to come back to the Holy Land. It's revived precious old memories and given me some valuable new ones. I'm so grateful to you for allowing me to join your pilgrimage, at my age always a risk.'

'We felt privileged to have you with us, Ralph,' Bob said. 'Your wide knowledge of the Middle East and first-hand experience of Palestine at the end of the Mandate were very much appreciated. Several of my parishioners told me how interesting they found your talk and being able to discuss it with you afterwards.'

That night Ralph felt very weak and could not get to sleep. His mind was full of thoughts. Why had he come back to Palestine? Partly because he wanted to return to the cradle of Christianity, but also because of his memories of the Holy Land—his first job, the stress and violence of the situation, the start of his friendship with Major Mac, his sight of Mary's photograph and his brush with death. His return had already produced an unexpected dividend in his meeting with the granddaughter of the lady who had treated his wound.

Eventually he dozed off, only to dream, for the second time

during the pilgrimage, of being in the lifeboat on the Atlantic again. The cargo vessel had departed, and the waves whipped up by the strengthening wind were threatening to sink them. The Indian sailors were lying groaning at the bottom of the boat. Kathy and Ronnie were there, and Father John was encouraging them to say the Lord's Prayer. As they did so, the wind dropped a little and the aspect of the sea changed to that of the Sea of Galilee as he had seen it a few days before. It was still stormy and some of his fellow pilgrims looked fearful, but instead of Father John there was a figure in the bows of the boat who seemed to radiate authority and calm. Ralph looked up at him and knew that the wind and waves would never frighten him again.

Acknowledgements

While Chapter 1 is based partly on my childhood experience of being sent to South Africa by ship in 1940, I also acknowledge my debt to Elspeth Huxley's *Atlantic Ordeal, The Story of Mary Cornish* (Chatto and Windus, 1941). My character Kathy fulfils the same role as did Mary Cornish, an 'escort' on *The City of Benares* in September 1940, but is fictional, as are the other characters in this book. I am grateful to Asssociated Press for their permission to use the photograph on the cover. I should like to thank Lesley Jones for her valuable editorial advice.

Antony Hornyold